Workbook
and Answer Key

Editorial Offices: Glenview, Illinois • Parsippany, New Jersey • New York, New York
Sales Offices: Parsippany, New Jersey • Duluth, Georgia • Glenview, Illinois
Coppell, Texas • Sacramento, California • Mesa, Arizona

www.sfsocialstudies.com

Program Authors

Dr. Candy Dawson Boyd
Professor, School of Education
Director of Reading Programs
St. Mary's College
Moraga, California

Dr. Geneva Gay
Professor of Education
University of Washington
Seattle, Washington

Rita Geiger
Director of Social Studies and
    Foreign Languages
Norman Public Schools
Norman, Oklahoma

Dr. James B. Kracht
Associate Dean for
    Undergraduate Programs
    and Teacher Education
College of Education
Texas A&M University
College Station, Texas

Dr. Valerie Ooka Pang
Professor of Teacher Education
San Diego State University
San Diego, California

Dr. C. Frederick Risinger
Director, Professional
    Development and Social
    Studies Education
Indiana University
Bloomington, Indiana

Sara Miranda Sanchez
Elementary and Early
    Childhood Curriculum
    Coordinator
Albuquerque Public Schools
Albuquerque, New Mexico

Contributing Authors

Dr. Carol Berkin
Professor of History
Baruch College and the
    Graduate Center
The City University of New York
New York, New York

Lee A. Chase
Staff Development Specialist
Chesterfield County
    Public Schools
Chesterfield County, Virginia

Dr. Jim Cummins
Professor of Curriculum
Ontario Institute for Studies
    in Education
University of Toronto
Toronto, Canada

Dr. Allen D. Glenn
Professor and Dean Emeritus
Curriculum and Instruction
College of Education
University of Washington
Seattle, Washington

Dr. Carole L. Hahn
Professor, Educational Studies
Emory University
Atlanta, Georgia

Dr. M. Gail Hickey
Professor of Education
Indiana University-Purdue
    University
Fort Wayne, Indiana

Dr. Bonnie Meszaros
Associate Director
Center for Economic Education
    and Entrepreneurship
University of Delaware
Newark, Delaware

ISBN 0-328-08187-6

Contents

Main Idea and Details

Learning to find the main idea and details will help you understand most kinds of writing. The most important idea about a topic is its main idea. The ideas that give more information about the main idea are its supporting details.

Directions: Read the paragraph. Then read each question. Fill in the circle next to the correct answer.

One reason the United States is so diverse is that immigrants have come here from all over the world. About 1,000 years ago, Europeans began traveling to North America as explorers. Five hundred years ago Spain, sent explorers such as Christopher Columbus and Juan Ponce de León. The French were soon to follow. French explorers Jacques Cartier and Samuel de Champlain landed in what is now Canada. The English then sent explorers John Cabot and Henry Hudson, among others. They hoped to catch up with the French and Spanish in the race to establish colonies in North America. Many people also arrived from Africa. Today people from around 200 different countries live in the United States.

---

1. What is the main idea of the paragraph?
   Ⓐ Portugal was the first to send out explorers.
   Ⓑ About 500 years ago, Europeans began traveling to explore the Americas.
   Ⓒ One reason the United States is so diverse is that immigrants have come here from all over the world.
   Ⓓ People from around 200 different countries live in the U.S. today.

2. Which explorer helped the English try to catch up to its rival explorers?
   Ⓐ Christopher Columbus
   Ⓑ John Cabot
   Ⓒ Hernando de Soto
   Ⓓ Samuel de Champlain

3. Which country sent Columbus and Ponce de León?
   Ⓐ France
   Ⓑ England
   Ⓒ Portugal
   Ⓓ Spain

Notes for Home: Your child learned to identify the main idea and details of an assigned reading selection.
Home Activity: With your child, skim a brief newspaper article. Ask your child to identify the main idea and details of the story.

Vocabulary Preview

Directions: Match each vocabulary word to its meaning. Write the vocabulary word on the line after the definition. You may use your glossary. Not all words will be used.

culture
ideal
ethnic group
census
immigrant
democracy
republic
constitution
citizen
private property
economy
free enterprise
profit
supply
demand
export
import

1. a good that one country buys from another

   _____

2. a good that one country sells to another _____

3. written plan of government _____

4. all the things that surround us, including air, water, land, trees

   _____

5. amount of a product that is available _____

6. business of growing crops and raising animals

   _____

7. government's count of the people in a country

   _____

8. fuel formed from the remains of plants and animals that lived thousands of years ago _____

9. government in which the people elect representatives to make laws and run the government _____

10. important belief _____

11. large area with common features that set it apart from other areas _____

12. member of a country _____

13. method of bringing water to dry land _____

14. moisture that falls to Earth in the form of rain, sleet, or snow

    _____

15. money a business has left over after it has paid all its costs

    _____

| consumer |
| entrepreneur |
| region |
| geography |
| agriculture |
| irrigation |
| climate |
| precipitation |
| interdependent |
| natural resource |
| mineral |
| fossil fuel |
| renewable resource |
| nonrenewable resource |
| conservation |
| environment |
| pollution |

16. economy in which people start their own businesses and own their own property _____

17. person who leaves one country to go live in another _____

18. people who share customs and language _____

19. person who buys or uses goods and services _____

20. person who starts a new business, hoping to make a profit _____

21. preserving and protecting resources _____

22. resource that can be replaced _____

23. resource that cannot easily be replaced _____

24. the way of life of a group of people _____

25. something owned by an individual _____

26. substance found on Earth that is neither animal nor vegetable _____

27. system for producing goods and services _____

28. addition of harmful substances to the air, water, or soil _____

29. weather in an area over a long period of time _____

30. the study of Earth and how people use it _____

Notes for Home: Your child learned several terms that are helpful when studying the United States.
Home Activity: Write definitions and terms on separate index cards. Play a matching game to build comprehension of each word.

Name _____ Date _____

Lesson 1: The American People

Directions: Answer the following questions on the lines provided. You may use your textbook.

1. What is the meaning of the motto, or short saying, on the Great Seal?

_____

_____

2. The motto on our nation's Great Seal was representative of the United States when it first became a country. Why do you think the motto still represents our country today?

_____

_____

3. What are the two largest ethnic groups in the United States today?

_____

_____

4. What are two reasons early immigrants left their homelands and came to the land known today as the United States?

_____

_____

5. What do you think the words "indivisible, with liberty and justice for all," found at the end of the Pledge of Allegiance, mean?

_____

_____

_____

Notes for Home: Your child learned that the people of the United States share many ideals.
Home Activity: Discuss the importance of symbols to this country. With your child, review citizens' responsibilities in upholding the Pledge of Allegiance.

Name _____ Date _____

Read Line and Circle Graphs

Graphs show information in a visual way. A line graph shows change over time. A circle graph shows a whole divided into parts. These graphs use rounded numbers.

Directions: Read each graph and answer the questions that follow.

Population of Western United States 1990–2000

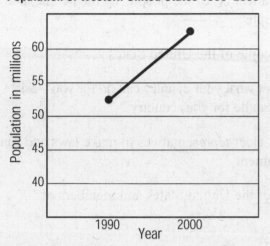

Population of Southern United States 1990–2000

1. Did the population of the West increase or decrease from 1990 to 2000? Explain how you know.

_____

2. By how much did the population of the South change from 1990 to 2000?

_____

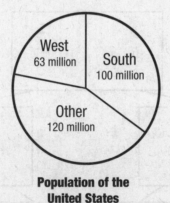

Population of the United States (rounded)

3. Where do the fewest people live?

_____

Notes for Home: Your child learned to read line and circle graphs.
Home Activity: With your child, review the information shown on a line or circle graph in the newspaper or a magazine. Discuss how the labels on the graphs support the visuals.

Lesson 2: Government by the People

Directions: Draw a line from each item in column A to its example in column B.

Column A

1. republic

2. Abraham Lincoln

3. John F. Kennedy

4. United States Constitution

5. elected representatives

Column B

a. our government is "of the people, by the people, and for the people"

b. "We the people of the United States . . ."

c. ". . . ask not what your country can do for you—ask what you can do for your country."

d. the people elect representatives to make laws and run the government

e. President of the United States and members of Congress

Directions: Complete the flow chart using the terms in the box.

freedom of religion	obey the law	right to vote
freedom of speech	respect the rights of others	rights
involvement in government	responsibilities	

Notes for Home: Your child learned about the roles and responsibilities of citizenship in a democracy.
Home Activity: Review this lesson with your child. Together, make a list of the rights and responsibilities of Americans to their country.

Name _____ Date _____

Lesson 3: Free Enterprise

The economy of the United States is based on the system of free enterprise. Under this system, individuals are free to start their own businesses and own their own property.

Directions: Explain each term and tell how it relates to free enterprise. Write your answers on the lines provided. You may use your textbook.

1. economy

_____

_____

_____

2. profit

_____

_____

_____

3. supply and demand

_____

_____

_____

4. export and import

_____

_____

_____

5. consumer

_____

_____

_____

Notes for Home: Your child learned about the free enterprise system.
Home Activity: Review with your child two or three business advertisements in your local telephone book. Apply each term above to a discussion of free enterprise, and what this concept means to the businesses you've chosen.

Lesson 4: Land and Regions

Directions: Write the name of the region described on the lines provided. Some regions are described more than once.

Northeast	Southeast	Midwest	Southwest	West

1. This region is divided into two smaller regions—New England and the Middle Atlantic states.

   _____

2. The Grand Canyon is in this region.

   _____

3. The nation's largest city, New York City, is located in this region.

   _____

4. Some of the country's highest mountains are in this region.

   _____

5. Two of the nation's largest port cities, Baton Rouge and New Orleans, Louisiana, are located in this region.

   _____

6. Big Bend National Park is located in this region.

   _____

7. This region produces more corn than any other region in the country.

   _____

8. This region of the United States is the largest in area.

   _____

 Notes for Home: Your child learned the five regions of the United States.
Home Activity: With your child, review the map on pp. 26–27. Discuss the geography and the climate of the region in which you live.

Read an Elevation Map

An elevation map shows the elevation, or height, of land. Elevation is measured above or below sea level. The map shows the elevation for the states of Massachusetts and Rhode Island.

Directions: Read the map and answer the questions that follow.

1. At what elevation range are most of the large cities on this map found? _____

2. What is the elevation of Boston, Massachusetts? _____

3. Starting at Mt. Greylock, how many feet would a person have to descend to reach sea

   level? _____

4. Which labeled river in Massachusetts is at the highest elevation? _____

Notes for Home: Your child learned to read an elevation map.
Home Activity: With your child, use an elevation map to identify areas in the United States with the highest or lowest elevations. Discuss the concept of sea level, at 0 feet of elevation.

Use with Pages 34–38.

Lesson 5: Resources and the Environment

Directions: Complete the chart with information from this lesson.

Important Resources	Why They Are Important	Two Examples
natural resources		
minerals		
fossil fuels		
renewable resources		
nonrenewable resources		
national parks		

Notes for Home: Your child learned about America's reliance on its natural resources.
Home Activity: Walk around your home with your child. Identify the renewable and nonrenewable resources your family consumes regularly.

Vocabulary Review

Directions: Choose the vocabulary word from the box that best completes each sentence. Write the word on the line provided. Not all words will be used.

culture	private property	entrepreneur	mineral
ideal	economy	region	fossil fuel
ethnic group	free enterprise	geography	renewable resource
census	profit	agriculture	nonrenewable resource
immigrant	supply	irrigation	conservation
democracy	demand	climate	environment
republic	export	precipitation	pollution
constitution	import	interdependent	
citizen	consumer	natural resource	

1. A _____ tells how many people live in a country.

2. Someone who moves to another country is an _____.

3. A written plan of government is known as a _____.

4. A _____ is a member of a country.

5. Our economy is based on a system of _____.

6. Entrepreneurs start businesses to earn a _____.

7. Import and _____ is buying and selling goods between countries.

8. Each person who buys or uses a good is a _____.

9. _____ can help farmers grow crops in dry areas.

10. _____ is the weather of a certain place over a period of time.

Notes for Home: Your child learned several terms related to the republic of the United States.
Home Activity: Have your child restate key concepts of this chapter to you, using the above terms in the descriptions.

Overview Project   As History Unfolds

Use with Page 44.

Directions: In a group, plan how to keep a record of what you learn in your social studies class for the school year.

1. On the following lines, list any materials your group needs to make your booklet.

   _____   _____   _____

   _____   _____   _____

2. Sketch how your booklet will look in the following boxes.

3. Identify how each group member will help create the booklet.

Name	Task		Name	Task

4. Agree upon a schedule of how often the group will meet to add information and pictures to

   the booklet. We will meet _____.

✔ Checklist for Students

_____ We made a list of materials needed to make the booklet.

_____ We agreed upon a design for the booklet.

_____ We assigned tasks to each group member.

_____ We made a schedule to meet and work on the booklet.

Notes for Home: In a group, your child will create a booklet to record what they learn in social studies this year.
Home Activity: Review this record with your child. Confirm how your child will participate and what responsibilities will be completed according to the schedule.

Summarize

A summary tells the main ideas of a paragraph, section, or story. A good summary is short and tells the most important ideas. It should not include many words or details.

Directions: Read the paragraph. Then answer the questions that follow. Fill in the circle next to the correct answer.

Many scholars believe that people first migrated to the Americas in different ways. Some believe that the Bering Strait became shallower, exposing the land below the water and forming a land bridge between Asia and the Americas. Others believe that people arrived by boat. Despite questions as to how they arrived, people believe that the first Americans moved from North America to South America. They adapted to their new environments by changing their way of living to meet the challenges of each environment.

---

1. Which sentence is the BEST summary of the paragraph?

   Ⓐ Many scholars believe that people migrated to the Americas, moving from north to south, and adapting their culture to meet their environment.

   Ⓑ Some people believe that the Bering Strait became shallower, exposing a land bridge between Asia and the Americas.

   Ⓒ People moved to new environments, adapting their lifestyle to their environment.

   Ⓓ Some people believe the first people to migrate to America arrived by boat.

2. In which part of the paragraph do you look to find the summary?

   Ⓐ detail

   Ⓑ body text

   Ⓒ last sentence

   Ⓓ topic sentence

3. Which is important to include in a summary?

   Ⓐ all names, dates, and facts

   Ⓑ supporting details

   Ⓒ name of the source or author

   Ⓓ main ideas

Notes for Home: Your child learned to summarize a paragraph, section, or story.
Home Activity: Have your child summarize the day's activities, giving the most important ideas with few words or details.

Vocabulary Preview

Directions: Match each vocabulary word to its meaning. Write the vocabulary word on the line after the definition. You may use your glossary.

Ice Age	artifact	drought	pyramid
glacier	archaeologist	civilization	empire
migrate	ceremony	surplus	tribute
theory	mesa	specialize	slavery

1. a long period without rain _____

2. thick sheets of ice _____

3. movement of people to another land _____

4. a possible explanation _____

5. an object that someone made in the past _____

6. do only one kind of job _____

7. activity done for a special purpose or event _____

8. high, flat landform that rises steeply from the land around it _____

9. culture with organized system of government, religion, and learning _____

10. long period of extreme cold on Earth _____

11. a group of lands and peoples ruled by one leader _____

12. the practice of holding people against their will _____

13. more than is needed _____

14. payment demanded by rulers from the people they rule _____

15. one who studies artifacts of people _____

16. building shaped like a triangle _____

Notes for Home: Your child learned terms about early life in the Western Hemisphere.
Home Activity: Help your child learn these terms by making flashcards (with a term on one side and the definition on the other) to review each word.

Lesson 1: Migration to the Americas

Directions: Complete the cause-and-effect chart, using the phrases in the box.

- Much of Earth's water was frozen into glaciers
- Agriculture made it possible for people to settle in one place
- A land bridge linked Asia to America
- Archaeologists study artifacts
- The large animals were no longer available to hunters
- Their way of life centered on hunting
- Animals crossed the land bridge to North America

Cause	Effect
	and the level of Earth's oceans dropped.
	and people and animals migrated to the Americas.
	so hunters followed them.
	so hunters moved often.
	and draw conclusions about people from long ago.
	and hunters became hunter-gatherers.
	because people began to grow their food.

Notes for Home: Your child learned how people migrated to the Americas.
Home Activity: Have your child share examples of cause-and-effect relationships in his or her daily life.

Read Climographs

Directions: Read the climograph and answer the questions that follow.

	Temperature		Precipitation	
	°F	°C	in.	cm.
January	30	-1	3	8.2
February	32	0	3	6.9
March	41	5	4	11.2
April	52	11	4	10.2
May	61	16	4	11.0
June	70	21	4	9.9
July	74	23	4	11.0
August	72	22	4	10.2
September	66	19	3	8.0
October	54	12	3	6.9
November	42	6	3	8.2
December	32	0	3	7.8

1. What two kinds of information are shown in a climograph?

   _____

2. Which two months shown have the same average temperature?

   _____

3. What is the warmest month on the climograph?

   _____

4. Which month has the lowest average temperature?

   _____

5. Which month has the highest average precipitation?

   _____

6. Which months are the driest?

   _____

Notes for Home: Your child learned to read a climograph.
Home Activity: Draw a climograph like the one shown. With your child, plot the daily high and low temperatures and precipitation in your area for a week.

Lesson 2: Early American Cultures

Directions: Match each clue to its culture. Write the name of the culture on the line. Some cultures will be used more than once. You may use your textbook.

Mound Builders **Anasazi** **Inuit**

1. We are several groups who lived east of the Mississippi River. _____

2. We developed the kayak. _____

3. We are also known as the "Cliff Dwellers." _____

4. We built the Great Serpent Mound. _____

5. Our religious ceremonies were held in kivas, and only men were allowed to

   enter. _____

6. Artifacts tell archaeologists that trade was important to us. Artifacts came

   from the north, south, east, and west. _____

7. We lived in houses made from blocks of packed snow. _____

8. We were first to use irrigation in what would be the United States.

   _____

9. Today we live in the frozen lands near the Arctic Ocean. _____

10. We lived in the Four Corners area for approximately 1,200 years.

    _____

 Notes for Home: Your child learned about early American cultures.
Home Activity: Have your child compare and contrast elements of early American cultures to your own. How are they alike and different?

Lesson 3: The Rise of Empires

Directions: Complete the Venn diagram by writing the terms and phrases in the box in the correct section of the diagram. You may use your textbook.

roads linked to capital city	Atlantic to Pacific empire	present-day Peru
fastest communication system	worshipped many gods	floating gardens
one of the world's largest cities	system of writing	terraces
worshipped god of war	pyramids	farmers
people specialized	calendar	conquerors
produced food surplus		

Maya

Inca

Aztec

Notes for Home: Your child learned about civilizations developing in Mexico, Central America, and South America.
Home Activity: Have your child draw a Venn diagram like the one shown. Complete it together to compare the activities of three people in your household in a day.

Name _____ Date _____

Vocabulary Review

Directions: Choose the vocabulary word from the box that best completes each sentence. Write the word on the line provided. Not all words will be used.

Ice Age	artifact	drought	pyramid
glacier	archaeologist	civilization	empire
migrate	ceremony	surplus	tribute
theory	mesa	specialize	slavery

1. The ruler demanded that his people pay him _____.

2. An _____ is a person who studies people from long ago.

3. A thick sheet of ice is known as a _____.

4. The ruler's vast _____ contained many peoples and lands.

5. A stone arrowhead made long ago is an _____.

6. The lack of rain caused a _____ and problems for farmers.

7. The Maya _____ developed an extremely accurate calendar.

8. The Anasazi people _____ in basket weaving.

9. The _____ was an extremely cold period of time on Earth.

10. A building shaped like a triangle with the point at the top is called a

    _____.

11. Animals and people move, or _____, to new lands.

12. _____ is when people are held against their will and do not have their freedom.

13. The unneeded _____ food was traded for needed things.

14. The landform known as a _____ means table in Spanish.

Notes for Home: Your child learned terms about early life in the Western Hemisphere.
Home Activity: Have your child use these vocabulary words to tell you a story about early civilizations.

Vocabulary Preview

Directions: Match the underlined vocabulary word to its meaning. Write the letter for the meaning of each underlined word on the line. You may use your glossary.

1. Members of a <u>tribe</u> share a common culture. _____

2. People on the hunt lived in <u>tepees</u>. _____

3. <u>Wampum</u> belts and necklaces are special. _____

4. The <u>shaman</u> will cure your illness. _____

5. The Iroquois lived in the Eastern Woodlands <u>cultural region</u>. _____

6. The people formed a <u>league</u> to support peace. _____

7. The <u>totem pole</u> showed a person's wealth. _____

8. The <u>Pueblo</u> Indians developed a village way of life. _____

9. A Plains Indian lived in a <u>lodge</u>. _____

10. The hosts of the <u>potlatch</u> gave gifts. _____

11. You can see traditional dances at a <u>powwow</u>. _____

12. They used a <u>travois</u> to carry the buffalo. _____

13. Many Native Americans live on a <u>reservation</u>. _____

14. A <u>longhouse</u> is an Iroquois building used for shelter. _____

a. Round hut built over a deep hole

b. Group of families with one leader

c. Organization for a specific purpose

d. Very long Iroquois building

e. Polished seashells on strings or woven into belts

f. Shelter made of a circle of poles and buffalo hides

g. Poles to which a load was tied for transport

h. Land set aside by the U.S. government

i. Healer

j. Spanish word for *village*

k. American Indian gathering to keep traditions alive

l. Type of party; word meaning "to give away"

m. Area in which people with similar cultures live

n. A carved post with animals or other images

Notes for Home: Your child learned about terms related to Native Americans.
Home Activity: With your child, select one Native American group and find out about its culture.

Name _____ Date _____

Lesson 1: The Eastern Woodlands

Directions: Answer the following questions on the lines provided.

1. What did members of the Seneca, Cayuga, Onondaga, Oneida, Mohawk, and

   Tuscarora tribes share? _____

   _____

2. What was the purpose of the Iroquois League?

   _____

3. What were the different roles of men and women in the Iroquois League?

   _____

   _____

   _____

4. How did the Iroquois use the natural resources of the Woodlands? Name at least three ways.

   _____

   _____

   _____

5. What is one way the Iroquois today have changed? What is one way they are the same as in their past?

   _____

   _____

   _____

   _____

 Notes for Home: Your child learned about the American Indians of the Eastern Woodlands and the Iroquois League.
Home Activity: Have your child compare ways Native Americans gave thanks to practices in your culture.

Lesson 2: The Great Plains

Directions: Answer the following questions on the lines provided.

1. What effect did dry land have on the Plains Indians?

_____

_____

_____

2. How were the Plains Indians' lives affected by the buffalo?

_____

_____

_____

_____

3. What methods did the Plains Indians use to hunt buffalo?

_____

_____

_____

4. How did the Cheyenne use horses?

_____

_____

_____

5. In which present-day state do many of the Cheyenne live?

_____

_____

_____

Notes for Home: Your child learned about the tribes of the Great Plains.
Home Activity: Have your child explain how the horse changed the lives of the American Indians.

Internet Research

Directions: Answer the following questions on the lines provided.

1. Why is it important to use only reliable reference sources when doing research on the Internet?

_____

_____

2. When searching on the Internet, what is the effect of putting a phrase in quotes?

_____

_____

3. What is one disadvantage of doing research on the Internet?

_____

_____

_____

4. What is one advantage of doing research on the Internet?

_____

_____

Directions: Complete the flowchart using the sentences in the box.

Pick Web sites to visit.	Choose a topic.	Choose a search engine.
Type in the keywords.	Narrow the search, if necessary.	

Notes for Home: Your child learned about doing research on the Internet.
Home Activity: Work with your child on your home or local library computer to research a topic of your child's choice.

Lesson 3: The Southwest Desert

Directions: Match each term in the box to its description. Write the term on the line. Some terms will be used more than once.

| Apache | Navajo | Pueblo Indians | kachina | snake dance | Oraibi |

1. Ceremony that dancers hope will bring rain

   _____

2. Lived a village way of life based on farming

   _____

3. Thought to be descendents of the Anasazi

   _____

4. A tribe of hunters

   _____

5. Hopi and Zuni tribes

   _____

6. A tribe who raised sheep

   _____

7. Dolls used to educate young Hopi about their religion

   _____

8. Hopi village built on a mesa

   _____

Notes for Home: Your child learned about the tribes of the Southwest.
Home Activity: Help your child draw a picture or use modeling clay to make a Pueblo village.

Lesson 4: The Northwest Coast

Directions: Explain each term. Tell how each item was used by the people of the Northwest Coast. Write your answers on the lines provided. You may use your textbook.

1. potlatch

_____

_____

2. hunting and gathering

_____

_____

3. totem pole

_____

_____

_____

4. dugout canoe

_____

_____

5. blankets and copper shields

_____

_____

6. shaman

_____

_____

7. masks, rattles, and serving dishes carved from wood

_____

_____

 Notes for Home: Your child learned about tribes of the Northwest Coast.
Home Activity: Review the above items with your child. Together, rank each item from 1 to 7 to indicate how important each item was to the people of the Northwest Coast.

Vocabulary Review

Directions: Choose the vocabulary word from the box that best completes each sentence. Write the word on the line provided.

tribe	wampum	travois	totem pole
league	reservation	powwow	shaman
cultural region	lodge	pueblo	
longhouse	tepee	potlatch	

1. The son carved a _____ to show his ancestry and wealth.

2. The goods and belongings were carried on a _____.

3. The _____ used special items to cure people.

4. All the members of the _____ listened to the chief.

5. While out on a hunt, the women put up the _____.

6. A _____ can be as long as half a football field.

7. A _____ is a building in which the Plains Indians lived.

8. They will host a _____ with gifts for everyone.

9. They formed a _____ to make peace.

10. Some Native Americans today still live on a _____.

11. You may be able to buy _____ at the _____.

12. _____ is the Spanish word for *village* and the name of a group of people

who lived in the Southwest Desert _____.

Notes for Home: Your child learned about terms related to Native Americans.
Home Activity: Quiz your child on proper spelling and usage of these vocabulary words.

Name _____ Date _____

Vocabulary Preview

Directions: Read each sentence. Match the underlined word in each sentence with its synonym or definition below. Write the word on the line. You may use your glossary.

The <u>emperor</u> ruled the people fairly.

The sailors used a <u>magnetic compass</u> to find their way home.

The people in the <u>caravan</u> brought gold and other goods to the city.

The people went on a <u>pilgrimage</u> to the holy land.

The <u>astrolabe</u> helped map makers.

The <u>saga</u> has been told for thousands of years.

A great deal of growth took place during the <u>Renaissance</u>.

Sailors use <u>navigation</u> to guide their ships.

Many people were captured and sold in the <u>slave trade</u>.

---

1. _____ Long spoken tale repeated from one generation to the next

2. _____ Tool used by sailors to determine their direction at sea

3. _____ Science sailors use to plot their course and find their location far from land

4. _____ Group of traders traveling together

5. _____ Buying and selling of human beings

6. _____ Journey taken for religious reasons

7. _____ Ruler of an empire

8. _____ Tool that used the sun and stars to find a location based on its distance from the equator

9. _____ Period of time that marked a new beginning in arts and sciences and a desire to learn more about the world

---

 Notes for Home: Your child learned terms about early life in the Eastern Hemisphere.
Home Activity: With your child, read a newspaper article about scientific exploration. Discuss the tools scientists used to make their discoveries.

Lesson 1: Traveling Asia's Silk Road

Directions: Match each term to one explorer. Write the term on a line on the graphic organizer.

Africa	gunpowder	India	silk cloth
China, 1405	paper money	Red Sea	Silk Road
coal	magnetic compass	sailor	Venice, 1271
East Indies	Persian Empire	merchant	tea and spices

Notes for Home: Your child learned about the journeys of Marco Polo and Zheng He.
Home Activity: Visit the local library or search the Internet with your child to find out more about one of the places mentioned in this lesson.

Lesson 2: Africa's Trading Empires

Directions: Answer the following questions on the lines provided. You may use your textbook.

1. Why was Ghana willing to trade gold for salt?

   _____

   _____

2. Why was Timbuktu an important place?

   _____

   _____

   _____

3. What was the religion of the Arab traders?

   _____

   _____

4. Who are Muslims?

   _____

   _____

5. How did Mali and Ghana gain their wealth?

   _____

   _____

6. What is the connection between Mansa Musa and Mecca?

   _____

   _____

   _____

Critical Thinking: The camel became known as the "ship of the desert." How does this term apply to camels?

   _____

   _____

   _____

   _____

Notes for Home: Your child learned how travel to different parts of the world connected people.
Home Activity: Scan travel ads in the newspaper with your child. Discuss the benefits of foreign travel.

Lesson 3: European Explorers

Directions: Match each item in Column A with its example in Column B. Write the number of the item on the line.

Column A	Column B
1. Explorers from Scandinavia	_____ Renaissance
2. Traveled to Greenland	_____ Prince Henry the Navigator
3. Spoken tale passed on from one generation to the next	_____ Calicut, India
4. Age that marked a new beginning in arts and sciences and a desire to learn more about the world	_____ Vasco da Gama
5. Invented the printing press	_____ Vikings
6. Portuguese ruler who took lead in 1420s in developing new trade route to Asia	_____ Johann Gutenberg
7. Buying and selling of human beings	_____ slave trade
8. Explorer whose ships were blown by storm around southern tip of Africa into Indian Ocean	_____ Bartolomeu Dias
9. Sailed to India in 1497	_____ Eric the Red
10. Portuguese merchants settled there, bought spices at low prices, and shipped them back to Europe	_____ saga

Notes for Home: Your child learned about people exploring new lands.
Home Activity: Use the dates in this lesson to make a time line of European explorers with your child.

Use Parallel Time Lines

Directions: The parallel time lines you used on pp. 116–117 are horizontal. Parallel time lines can also be vertical. Look at the vertical time lines on this page. Notice the dates and the continent each time line represents. Now look at the events in the box. Write each event in sequence on the correct country time line.

| 982: Eric the Red discovers Greenland |
| 1000: Leif Ericsson lands in North America |
| 1274: Marco Polo reaches China |
| 1350: Renaissance begins |
| 1400: China builds naval fleet |
| 1405: Zheng He leads Chinese fleet |
| 1420: Portuguese find new sea routes |
| 1433: Zheng He dies |
| 1450: Gutenberg develops printing press |
| 1498: Da Gama reaches India |

ASIA   **EUROPE**

900

1000

1100

1200

1300

1400

1500

Notes for Home: Your child learned to read and use parallel time lines.
Home Activity: With your child make parallel time lines for tomorrow's activities scheduled for you and your child.

Vocabulary Review

Directions: Choose the vocabulary word from the box that best completes each sentence. Write the word on the line provided.

emperor	pilgrimage	Renaissance
magnetic compass	astrolabe	navigation
caravan	saga	slave trade

1. The _____ crossed the desert on camelback.

2. My brother went on a _____ to Mecca last year.

3. The _____ of the journey to the new land was passed down from one generation to the next.

4. The _____ is a tool that uses stars to determine distance from the equator.

5. A _____ will help you locate north, south, east, and west.

6. _____ is a science sailors use to guide them on the ocean.

7. Many cultural advances took place during the _____.

8. The _____ ruled a vast empire.

9. _____, or the business of buying and selling human beings, has existed for many centuries.

Directions: Write an original paragraph in the space below. Use as many of the vocabulary words as you can.

_____

_____

_____

_____

Notes for Home: Your child learned terms about early life in the Eastern Hemisphere.
Home Activity: Encourage your child to use each vocabulary word in an original sentence.

Use with Page 124.

UN T 1 Project Early Cultures Documentary

Directions: Plan a documentary about an early eastern or western culture. In a group, create a storyboard that describes the culture. Present the storyboard to the whole class.

- The culture for our documentary is _____.
- The title of our documentary is _____.
- The (✔) shows the topics covered in our storyboard:

____ peak period   ____ rulers   ____ significant dates and events

____ trade   ____ population   ____ accomplishments

____ important monuments ____ important artifacts ____ other interesting facts

- Our storyboard plan is below. Each storyboard describes a different picture.

1	2	3	4
5	6	7	8

✔ Checklist for Students

_____ We chose an early culture.

_____ We gave the documentary a title.

_____ We sketched our storyboard about the culture.

_____ On a separate page, we wrote a paragraph describing each picture.

_____ Our group presented the storyboard for our documentary to the class.

Notes for Home: Your child learned about early cultures.
Home Activity: With your child, research the cultural background of your family. Using online references or primary sources, find out more about your cultural heritage.

Sequence

The sequence of events is the order in which things happen. Finding the sequence of events is especially helpful when you are reading about history. Dates and words such as *first, then, after, once, afterwards,* and *later* help signal the sequence of events.

Directions: Read the paragraph, and then read each question. Fill in the circle next to the correct answer.

> First, Spain sent ships across the Atlantic. Spanish explorer Christopher Columbus sailed in 1492. After Columbus's first voyage, Spain sent more explorers. The Spanish conquered the Aztecs in 1521. Almost 100 years after Columbus's first voyage, English colonists attempted to set up a colony on Roanoke Island in 1587. Later, in 1624, the Dutch started New Amsterdam.

1. Which of the following countries was the first to send explorers to the Americas?
   Ⓐ Spain
   Ⓑ France
   Ⓒ Holland
   Ⓓ England

2. In which year were the Aztecs conquered?
   Ⓐ 1624
   Ⓑ 1492
   Ⓒ 1521
   Ⓓ 1587

3. Who started New Amsterdam?
   Ⓐ the English
   Ⓑ the Spanish
   Ⓒ the French
   Ⓓ the Dutch

 Notes for Home: Your child has been learning to find the sequence of events in a passage.
Home Activity: Have your child use word and date clues to tell you about recent events and activities in his or her life.

Vocabulary Preview

Directions: Read each vocabulary word from Chapter 4 in the box below. Then write each word in its definition on the lines provided. You may use your textbook.

expedition	conquistador	convert	plantation	missionary
colony	ally	colonist	encomienda	mission
Columbian Exchange	conquest	society		

1. A _____ is a group of people forming a community.

2. A _____ is a religious settlement where a

   _____ group lives and works.

3. To _____ means to change.

4. A _____ is the capture or taking of something by force.

5. An _____ is a journey made for a special purpose.

6. An _____ is a friend who will help in a fight.

7. A _____ is a Spanish conqueror.

8. A _____ is a settlement far from the country that rules it.

9. A _____ is a person who lives in a colony.

10. The _____ is a movement of people, animals, plants, diseases, and ways of life between the Eastern Hemisphere and Western Hemisphere.

11. An _____ is a large piece of land, usually given to its owners by the king of Spain.

12. A _____ is a large farm with workers who live on the land they work.

Notes for Home: Your child learned about Spain's colonization of the Americas.
Home Activity: Practice saying, spelling, and using these vocabulary words correctly with your child.

Lesson 1: The Voyages of Columbus

Directions: Answer the questions below on the lines provided. You may use your textbook.

1. What was one possible reason the Europeans wanted to go to the Indies?

   _____

   _____

2. How did Columbus get the king and queen of Spain to pay for his expedition?

   _____

   _____

3. What are the names of the ships Columbus used in his first voyage?

   _____

4. About how long did it take Columbus and his crew to cross the Atlantic?

   _____

5. What is the name of the place historians believe Columbus reached first?

   _____

6. Why did Columbus lead more expeditions to the Americas, bringing with him people, animals, and other supplies?

   _____

   _____

7. How did the Columbian Exchange change the lives of the people involved?

   _____

   _____

   _____

   _____

Notes for Home: Your child learned about the effects of Columbus's voyages to the Americas.
Home Activity: Have your child explain how Columbus's voyages to the Americas affected people in Europe and the Americas.

Use Latitude and Longitude

Directions: Draw a line from each word to its meaning. You may use your glossary.

1. latitude

2. longitude

3. meridian

4. prime meridian

5. grid

a. another name for line of longitude

b. 0° longitude

c. set of crossing lines

d. imaginary lines that measure distances east and west of the prime meridian

e. imaginary lines that measure distances north and south of the equator

Directions: Identify the approximate location of each of the following places.

6. Bahama Islands _____

7. Canary Islands _____

8. Cádiz, Spain _____

9. Jamaica _____

Notes for Home: Your child learned to use latitude and longitude to locate places on a map.
Home Activity: With your child, use the atlas map of the United States to find your state and the general location of your city. Help your child identify the approximate latitude and longitude of these.

Lesson 2: Different Worlds Collide

Directions: Sequence the events in the order in which they took place by numbering them from 1–9. You may use your textbook.

_____ The Aztec empire falls to the conquistadors.

_____ Cortés gains allies on his way to Tenochtitlan.

_____ The Aztecs rise up and throw the Spanish out of their city.

_____ Moctezuma agrees to let Cortés stay in Tenochtitlan.

_____ Moctezuma is killed, perhaps by his own people.

_____ The Spanish destroy Tenochtitlan.

_____ Colonists in New Spain hope to gain wealth from farms, businesses, and gold and silver mines.

_____ Cortés leaves Cuba for Mexico to gain some of the Aztecs' wealth.

_____ The colony of New Spain is established.

Critical Thinking Why do you think Moctezuma allowed Cortés to stay in Tenochtitlan at first?

_____

_____

_____

_____

Notes for Home: Your child learned about how Spain conquered the Americas.
Home Activity: Discuss with your child Spain's advantages over the Aztecs and how the Spanish conquered great empires.

38 Lesson Review

Workbook

Lesson 3: Life in New Spain

Directions: Draw a line from each item in Column A to its example in Column B.

Column A	Column B
1. Cíbola	a. large piece of land, usually given by the king of Spain
2. Vásquez de Coronado	b. explored the American Southwest in search of Cíbola
3. peninsulares, creoles, mestizos	c. legendary rich kingdom in north of Mexico
4. plantation	d. three levels of colonial society in New Spain
5. encomienda	e. large farm with many workers who live on the land they work

Directions: Complete the cause-and-effect chart using the terms and phrases in the box.

Spanish need to replace Indian slaves	Encomienda system
European diseases, overwork, and mistreatment	Role of missionaries

Cause	Effect
	Forced slavery on Indians by making them work without pay or enough food
	Indians learned about Christianity
	Indians died out
	Spanish enslaved captured Africans

Notes for Home: Your child learned about Spain's settlement of New Spain.
Home Activity: Have your child restate advantages and disadvantages of Spain's efforts to colonize New Spain.

Vocabulary Review

Directions: Use vocabulary words from Chapter 4 to complete the crossword puzzle.

Across

2. person who teaches his or her religion to others who have different beliefs

4. the capture or taking of something by force

7. movement of people, animals, plants, diseases, and ways of life between the Eastern Hemisphere and Western Hemisphere

9. large piece of land, usually given to its owners by the king of Spain

11. person who lives in a colony

12. settlement far from the country that rules it

Down

1. religious settlement where missionaries live and work

3. to change

5. large farm with many workers who live on the land they work

6. journey made for a special purpose

7. Spanish conqueror

8. group of people forming a community

10. friend who will help in a fight

Notes for Home: Your child learned how Spain built an empire in the Americas.
Home Activity: Ask your child to use vocabulary from this chapter to explain Spain's activities in the 1500s.

Vocabulary Preview

Directions: Write each vocabulary word from Chapter 5 beside its example or description. You may use your glossary.

charter	House of Burgesses	persecution	dissenter
stock	Northwest Passage	Mayflower Compact	proprietor
cash crop	Pilgrim	Puritan	debtor
indentured servant	Separatist		

1. Document that permitted colonists to settle on land claimed by their ruler _____

2. Person who journeys for religious reasons _____

3. A person whose views differ from others' _____

4. Shares in a company often sold to raise money for the company _____

5. Pilgrims' written plan of government for their colony _____

6. Crop grown for profit _____

7. Waterway connecting the Atlantic and Pacific Oceans _____

8. Person who owes money _____

9. Unjust treatment to a person because of his or her beliefs _____

10. A person who agreed to work for someone for a certain amount of time in exchange for the cost of the ocean voyage to North America _____

11. Group from England who wanted to purify, or reform, the Church of England _____

12. Person who wanted to separate from the Church of England _____

13. Owner _____

14. The first law-making assembly in an English colony _____

Notes for Home: Your child learned about the struggle to found colonies in North America.
Home Activity: Ask your child to use new vocabulary from this chapter to tell you about the struggle people faced to found America's first colonies.

Lesson 1: Hard Times in Virginia

Directions: Identify the cause and effect in each chart. Label the items "Cause" or "Effect" in the spaces provided. Then draw an arrow between the boxes to show the correct direction. The first one has been done for you.

1. Cause	Effect
White returned to England seeking aid for the colonists in Roanoke. He arrived to find Spain and England at war and England with no ships to send supplies to the colonists.	White returned to Roanoke only to find that the colonists had mysteriously disappeared.

2.	
English ships were smaller than Spanish ships and could move faster. The English had more powerful guns than the Spanish.	The English won the Battle of the Spanish Armada and became one of the world's most powerful nations.

3.	
Jamestown settlers began to die almost as soon as they arrived.	Jamestown was located on low, swampy land where disease-carrying mosquitoes lived. The water was not healthy to drink.

4.	
The men at Jamestown spent their days searching for gold. They did not plant crops or build housing.	Men died of starvation and disease. John Smith took over, and under his guidance the colonists survived.

5.	
Jamestown grew rapidly.	Tobacco grew well in Virginia and became a cash crop as exports rose.

Notes for Home: Your child learned about the first English colonies in North America.
Home Activity: Have your child explain the causes and effects of events that took place during the early days at Roanoke and Jamestown.

Lesson 2: New European Colonies

Directions: The French and the Dutch settled colonies in North America. Classify terms that relate to the French and the Dutch by writing them in the appropriate columns.

beaver fur trading	Holland	New Netherland
Henry Hudson	Montreal	Quebec
Hudson River	New Amsterdam	Samuel de Champlain
Huron Indians	New France	St. Lawrence River

French	Dutch

Directions: Suppose you are an explorer with Champlain or Hudson. Use one of the lists above to write a diary entry from your expedition.

Notes for Home: Your child learned about French and Dutch settlements in North America.
Home Activity: Using the map on p. 166, trace the routes of the Champlain and Hudson expeditions with your child.

Lesson 3: The First Colonies

Directions: Answer the questions below about life in the first colonies in North America. You may use your textbook.

1. What was the reason the Pilgrims decided to flee England?

   _____

2. Why did the Pilgrims go to Massachusetts and not Virginia?

   _____

   _____

   _____

3. How did the Pilgrims become friends with the Wampanoag?

   _____

   _____

   _____

4. How did Squanto, the interpreter for Massasoit and the Pilgrims, learn English?

   _____

   _____

   _____

5. Why did the Pilgrims hold a celebration of thanksgiving?

   _____

   _____

   _____

6. Why did the Puritans leave England, and what colony did they build in New England?

   _____

   _____

 Notes for Home: Your child learned about the Pilgrims' first thanksgiving and the reasons people left England to colonize North America.
Home Activity: With your child, discuss your family's Thanksgiving traditions and their meaning.

Fact and Opinion

A **fact** is a statement that can be checked. It can be proved to be true. An **opinion** is a personal view. It cannot be proved to be true or false.

Directions: Read the excerpts that follow. Look for facts and opinions. Underline the facts and circle the opinions.

Samuel de Champlain sails his ship up the mighty St. Lawrence River, wondering where it will take him. He notes in his journal that this is "beautiful country, where there is good land covered with trees."

In 1621, Pilgrims and Native Americans celebrated a delicious feast of thanksgiving together.

Philadelphia was the first colonial city to be planned on paper before it was built. Penn wanted the city to have wide streets, with lots of trees and green spaces.

Today, Americans believe that people have the right to worship freely.

Directions: In the spaces provided, write one fact and one opinion about the Pilgrims' first winter.

Fact

_____

_____

_____

Opinion

_____

_____

_____

Notes for Home: Your child learned to separate fact from opinion.
Home Activity: Have your child explain how to distinguish fact from opinion and tell you sentence pairs to model the concept.

Lesson 4: The 13 English Colonies

Directions: Draw a line from each item in Column A to its description in Column B.

Column A	Column B
New England, Middle, and Southern Colonies	New York and New York City
Thick woods provided excellent timber for homes; coastal waters were rich in fish	The Middle Colonies
Breadbasket of the colonies	Dissenter forced by Puritans to leave Massachusetts; founder of Rhode Island
Rich soil produced valuable crops such as tobacco and rice	Georgia
Roger Williams	New England Colonies
England renamed New Netherland and New Amsterdam	Maryland
William Penn, a Quaker	The Southern Colonies
Large section of land north of Virginia, given to a Catholic landowner, for a colony	The three regions of the 13 Colonies
James Oglethorpe founded last English colony in North America with debtors; helped protect the Carolinas from the Spanish in Florida	Founder of Pennsylvania

Notes for Home: Your child learned about the geography of the 13 English colonies.
Home Activity: On a map of the eastern seaboard of the United States, locate with your child the sites of the 13 colonies.

Vocabulary Review

Directions: Use the terms in the box to complete each sentence with information from Chapter 5. You may use your textbook. Not all words will be used.

charter	Northwest Passage	Puritan
stock	Pilgrim	dissenter
cash crop	Separatist	proprietor
indentured servant	persecution	debtor
House of Burgesses	Mayflower Compact	

1. Tobacco was a _____ in Virginia.

2. The _____ called for just and equal laws for Plymouth.

3. Virginia's _____ was an important step toward self-government in the English colonies.

4. The company has sold 49 percent of its shares of _____.

5. The _____ was an imagined waterway connecting the Atlantic and Pacific Oceans.

6. Many settlers journeyed to North America to escape religious _____.

7. Settlers received a _____ from the king to settle the land.

8. Before landing the Mayflower, _____ leaders wrote a plan of government for their colony.

9. Anne Hutchinson was a _____ because her views were different from those of her leader.

10. A _____ of a parcel of property can give or deny others permission to enter.

Notes for Home: Your child learned about the 13 original colonies.
Home Activity: Ask your child to restate in his or her own words how the first colonies were founded.

Name _____ Date _____

UNIT
2 Project   Breaking News

Use with Page 192.

Directions: A Native American and a European explorer or settler meet for the first time. In your group, assign roles and act out the meeting. Have the reporter give an eyewitness report of this historic event. Present your work to the class.

1. The Native American group we selected is _____.

   The explorer's or settler's European country is _____.

2. My role is (✔ one):

   ____ Native American   ____ European explorer or settler   ____ News reporter

3. The Native American's first impressions of the European explorer or settler:

   _____

   _____

4. The European settler's first impressions of the Native American:

   _____

   _____

5. The news reporter's description of the meeting:

   _____

   _____

✔ **Checklist for Students**

____ We chose a Native American group from this unit.
____ We chose a European country of origin for the explorer or settler.
____ We wrote the first impressions of the Native American and European.
____ We wrote the news reporter's description.

 Notes for Home: Your child learned about early encounters between Native Americans and European explorers and settlers.
Home Activity: With your child, discuss how first impressions often are based on physical qualities. Analyze physical characteristics on which people might base a personal impression.

Compare and Contrast

Directions: Read the passage. Use the reading strategy of compare and contrast to answer the questions below. Fill in the circle next to the correct answer.

Slavery was very important to the economies of the Northern and Southern Colonies. Although comparisons can be made between the life of slaves in the North and the South, there were differences, too.

In the South, few slaves worked in cities. Most worked on plantations. The planter often required enslaved people to work day and night. In spite of the difficult conditions, many slaves still found time for music. They built drums and other instruments similar to ones from their native countries in Africa. This kept their African culture alive.

Some West African slaves knew how to grow rice. Some shared this knowledge with plantation owners. For example, in the Carolinas rice became a valuable crop on many plantations.

Not all slaves in the Southern Colonies tended the crops. Some were skilled craftspeople who did carpentry work, tailoring, and blacksmithing on large plantations. They worked the same long, hard hours as those who worked in the fields.

The life of slaves in the Northern Colonies was in some ways different from life in the South. Some slaves worked on farms, but most worked in cities and towns. Most were not farmers. Instead, they worked as cooks or servants in people's homes, as skilled craftspeople, and in stores and inns. Some slaves in the North were able to earn extra money by taking on extra jobs. It sometimes took years of extra work at night, but some enslaved people earned enough money to buy their freedom.

1. How did slavery in the Southern Colonies differ from slavery in the Northern Colonies?
   Ⓐ Slaves were owned by others.
   Ⓑ Slaves had restrictions placed on them.
   Ⓒ Families of slaves could be split up.
   Ⓓ Most slaves worked on plantations.

2. In what ways was the life of enslaved people across America similar?
   Ⓐ They worked night and day on farms.
   Ⓑ They earned extra money by teaching planters to grow rice.
   Ⓒ Slaves tried to keep up their African culture.
   Ⓓ They cooked meals for people who lived in cities.

Notes for Home: Your child learned how to compare and contrast information.
Home Activity: With your child, compare and contrast your weekday activities. How does your child's day compare and contrast with yours?

Vocabulary Preview

Directions: Match each vocabulary word to its meaning. Write the vocabulary word on the line after the definition. You may use your glossary.

apprentice	Middle Passage	Great Awakening
artisan	self-sufficient	almanac
triangular trade routes	town common	Stono Rebellion

1. A young person who learns a skill from a more experienced person

   _____

2. The second leg of a three-part voyage _____

3. A religious movement that revived many colonists' interest in religion

   _____

4. Routes shaped like giant triangles _____

5. Reference book with facts and figures _____

6. People who rely on themselves for most of what they need _____

7. An open space where sheep and cattle could graze _____

8. A skilled worker who makes things by hand _____

9. Fight between enslaved people and owners near a river in South Carolina

   _____

Directions: On a separate sheet of a paper, write a paragraph comparing and contrasting life in the Northern and Southern English Colonies. Use as many of the vocabulary words as you can in your paragraph.

_____

_____

_____

_____

Notes for Home: Your child learned about colonial life in the North American colonies.
Home Activity: Have your child use as many vocabulary words as possible to compare his or her life with that of a child in one of the original colonies.

Lesson 1: Working and Trading

Directions: Answer the following questions on the lines provided.

1. What were the advantages and disadvantages of being an apprentice?

_____

_____

_____

2. What was the job of an artisan?

_____

_____

3. How did a person become an artisan?

_____

_____

4. What was daily life like for children who grew up on farms during colonial times?

_____

_____

_____

_____

5. On what natural resources was the New England economy based? and the Southern economy? What industries developed?

_____

_____

_____

_____

Notes for Home: Your child learned how people worked and traded during colonial times.
Home Activity: Ask your child if he or she would have preferred to have been an apprentice or a farm worker in colonial times. Have your child explain the duties and responsibilities of his or her choice.

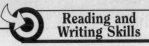
Read Newspapers

Newspapers are sources of news and events that are taking place now. They are usually printed daily or weekly. **News articles** are news stories based on facts about recent events. **Feature articles** have information about places, people, or events that would interest readers.

Directions: Label each topic as a news article or a feature article.

1. Movie reviews _____

2. Plane carrying emergency supplies lands safely _____

3. Ten worst traffic spots in metro area _____

4. Bridge opens to ease congestion _____

5. Movie star's wedding _____

6. Famous actor writes autobiography _____

7. Baby rescued by firefighters _____

8. Outdoor activities this weekend _____

9. Houses approved for the homeless _____

10. Historic building destroyed by flames _____

11. Presidential museum opens _____

12. Hay fever sufferers expect relief _____

13. Rising gas prices _____

14. Home remodeling tips _____

15. History of train exhibits _____

Notes for Home: Your child learned to identify the parts of a newspaper.
Home Activity: Look at a local newspaper with your child. As you skim it together, have your child classify stories as news or feature articles.

Lesson 2: Cities, Towns, and Farms

Directions: Match each term in the box to its description in the chart. Write the term in the second column in the chart.

Benjamin Franklin	Middle Colony towns	Puritans
Elizabeth Lucas Pinckney	general store	overseer
Southern plantation	town common	farming families
Philadelphia	meeting house	

Largest city in the 13 colonies	
Established first public library, hospital, and fire department in the 13 colonies	
First planter to raise a successful crop of indigo	
Began building towns in Massachusetts in 1630	
Open space where cattle and sheep could graze	
Plantation manager	
Most important building in colonial town	
Served as marketplaces where farmers could sell their crops and buy tools and clothes	
Large farm where cash crops such as tobacco and rice were grown	
Place to buy imported goods such as tea and sugar	
Families who had to make or grow most of what they needed	

Notes for Home: Your child learned about life in cities, towns, and on farms during colonial times.
Home Activity: Discuss with your child how colonial cities, towns, and farms compare with their modern-day counterparts.

Lesson 3: Everyday Life in the Colonies

Directions: Match the sentence fragments in Columns A and B to form complete sentences. Write the letter from Column B on the line in Column A.

Column A	Column B
1. Students learned the basics of reading, writing, arithmetic, and also learned the _____	a. they were considered a waste of paper, expensive, and were hard to make.
2. When children were not at school, they spent a lot of time doing _____	b. regions of the English Colonies.
3. Religion was an important part of life in all _____	c. chores around their family's house or farm.
4. The Great Awakening, which revived many colonists' interest in religion, also _____	d. common treats in the colonies, although all were not always tasty.
5. When the day's work was done, families often sat together and _____	e. rules of polite behavior.
6. Letter writing was important; however, envelopes were not used because _____	f. listened as a family member read aloud from a book.
7. Colonists learned to grow corn from Native Americans and _____	g. inspired people to help others.
8. Many desserts, such as donuts, ice cream, and fruit pies, were _____	h. used it to make breads, puddings, and pancakes.

Notes for Home: Your child learned about daily life during colonial times.
Home Activity: Ask your child to contrast schools in colonial times with his or her typical school day.

Lesson 4: Slavery in the Colonies

Directions: Write True or False next to each statement. If the statement is false, rewrite it to make it true.

1. Slaves in the South worked in stores, inns, and as skilled artisans. _____

   _____

2. In the North, slaves usually had more opportunities to improve their lives than did slaves

   in the South. _____

   _____

3. Slaves could travel or go onto a ship in small groups. _____

   _____

4. In the South, most slaves were forced to work on large plantations. _____

   _____

5. Some slaves showed planters how to raise rice, a valuable crop. _____

   _____

6. Some slaves were expert carpenters, blacksmiths, or tailors. _____

   _____

7. Slaves kept African culture alive by building drums, banjos, and other instruments. _____

   _____

8. Plantation owners were afraid that slaves were using instruments to celebrate when a slave

   escaped. _____

   _____

Notes for Home: Your child learned about the lives of slaves.
Home Activity: Ask your child how he or she would like to be treated by others.

Vocabulary Review

Directions: Circle the term in parentheses that best completes each sentence. You may use your glossary.

1. The (almanac, Great Awakening, Middle Passage) caused many colonists to become interested in religion once again and to help others.

2. A skilled worker, such as a carpenter or blacksmith, was an (apprentice, almanac, artisan).

3. The trade route from New England to West Africa to the West Indies and back to New England was a (Middle Passage, Stono Rebellion, triangular trade route).

4. A young person would spend years as an (almanac, apprentice, artisan), learning a skill from a more experienced person.

5. In colonial times people read (almanacs, apprentices, town commons), or reference books with facts and figures, for their valuable information.

6. The (Great Awakening, Stono Rebellion, triangular trade routes) took place when slaves clashed with their owners near a river in South Carolina.

7. The open space where sheep and cattle could graze in a town was known as the (triangular trade route, town common, Middle Passage).

8. The second leg of a three-part voyage was known as the (Middle Passage, Great Awakening, Stono Rebellion).

9. The New England Colonies were (triangular trade routes, apprentices, self-sufficient)— they relied on themselves for most of what they needed.

Directions: Describe the work life of a slave or an apprentice in the early English Colonies. Use as many vocabulary words as you can in your summary.

_____

_____

Notes for Home: Your child learned new terms related to life in colonial times.
Home Activity: With your child, discuss how people in colonial days tried to become self-sufficient. Discuss whether or not this goal is possible in today's society.

Vocabulary Preview

Directions: Read each sentence. Write a synonym or description for the underlined word on the line provided. You may use your glossary.

1. Wealthy ranchers in New Mexico built <u>haciendas</u>. _____

2. The soldiers held watch at the <u>presidio</u>. _____

3. Travelers followed <u>El Camino Real</u> between Mexico City and Santa Fe.

_____

4. The Pueblo fought intensely in the <u>Pueblo Revolt</u>.

_____

5. Beaver furs were exchanged for other goods at the <u>trading post</u>.

_____

6. The Allegheny is a <u>tributary</u> of the Ohio River.

_____

7. <u>King Philip's War</u> took place in New England. _____

_____

8. Many families moved to the <u>backcountry</u> so they could have their own land.

_____

9. The British won the <u>French and Indian War</u>. _____

_____

10. Many British died in <u>Pontiac's Rebellion</u>. _____

_____

11. The King hoped that the <u>Proclamation of 1763</u> would prevent further battles with the Native

Americans. _____

_____

 Notes for Home: Your child learned terms to describe the struggle for control of North America in the 1600s.
Home Activity: Have your child restate the reasons for these conflicts, using as many vocabulary words as possible.

Lesson 1: The Spanish Move North

Directions: Circle the term in parentheses that best completes each sentence. You may use your textbook.

1. The capital of New Spain was (Mexico City, Santa Fe).

2. In 1565, Pedro Menendez de Avilés led a small fleet of (British, Spanish) warships to Florida.

3. After a series of bloody battles between the (French, British) and the Spanish, Florida became part of New Spain.

4. After moving into Florida, the Spanish expanded into a region they called New Mexico. The town of (St. Augustine, Santa Fe) was founded and named the capital.

5. The Spanish hoped to find (cattle ranches, gold and silver) in New Mexico.

6. Spanish ranchers grazed (cattle, horses) on the grasses of the haciendas.

7. New Mexico was connected to Mexico City by (El Camino Real, the Rio Grande).

8. In 1680, a Pueblo leader named (Popé, Junípero Serra) led a revolt against the Spanish in New Mexico.

9. The white cross the Pueblo leader, Juan, carried to Santa Fe meant (surrender, battle).

10. In the fighting that became known as the Pueblo Revolt, the (Pueblo, Spanish) were driven out of New Mexico.

11. By 1692, the (Spanish, Pueblo) were able to recapture New Mexico.

12. The Spanish founded (San Antonio, St. Augustine) in 1718.

13. Father Junípero Serra founded Spanish (presidios, missions) in another part of New Spain, California.

Notes for Home: Your child learned about the Spanish struggle to take over North America.
Home Activity: Role-play the Pueblo Revolt with your child. Help him or her identify the points of view of the Spanish and the Pueblo.

Lesson 2: French Explore the Mississippi

Directions: Complete each sentence by copying the best ending from the box onto the lines provided.

---

he wanted to reach the mouth of the Mississippi River.

he made a map of the river and kept a journal of the experience.

it has an ideal location near the mouth of the Mississippi River.

control of the river would help them reach new lands where they could build trading posts.

he realized the river could not be the long-sought Northwest Passage because it continued to flow south.

---

1. The leaders of New France wanted to explore the Mississippi because

   _____

   _____

2. After traveling some 1,000 miles down the Mississippi, Marquette decided to return home

   because _____

   _____

3. Today we have an idea of some of the details of Marquette's journey down the Mississippi

   because _____

   _____

4. La Salle was willing to carry his canoe over snow and frozen streams because

   _____

5. New Orleans became a busy trading center because _____

   _____

 Notes for Home: Your child learned about the French exploration of the Mississippi River.
Home Activity: With your child, discuss the hardships explorers like Marquette and Jolliet faced on their voyages of discovery.

Name _____ Date _____

Compare Maps at Different Scales

Use with Pages 244–245.

In Chapter 5, you learned about the French colony of Montreal, in the present-day province of Quebec.

Directions: Answer the following questions on the lines provided.

1. Which map would you use to measure the distance from Montreal to Laval?

   _____

2. Which map would you use to locate McGill University?

   _____

3. About how far is it from Montreal to Longueuil—1 mile, 3 miles, or 20 miles?

   _____

4. What large road is near the Planetarium and the Convention Center?

   _____

Notes for Home: Your child learned to compare maps at different scales.
Home Activity: With your child, compare the areas shown by a standard road map (small scale) to a map of your neighborhood or subdivision (large scale). Discuss when it is best to use each map.

Lesson 3: The French and Indian War

Directions: Complete the cause-and-effect chart with information from your textbook.

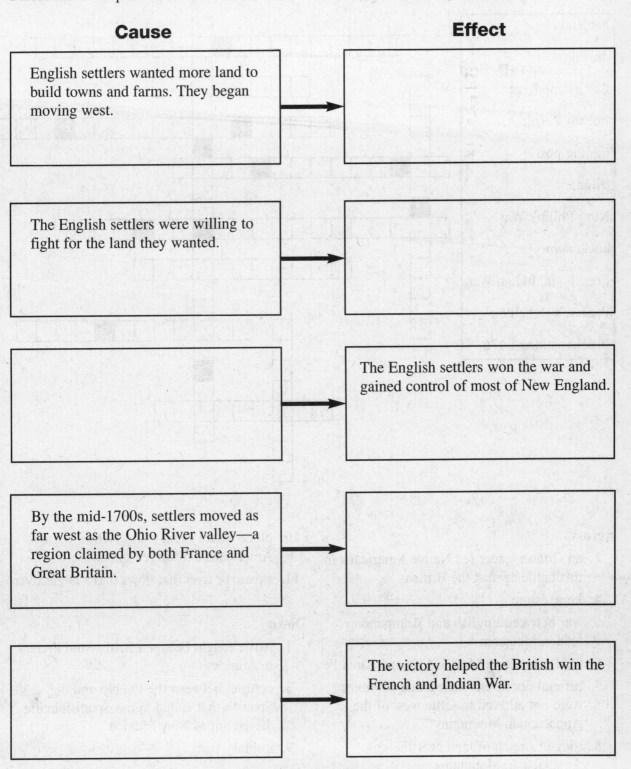

Cause

Effect

English settlers wanted more land to build towns and farms. They began moving west.

The English settlers were willing to fight for the land they wanted.

The English settlers won the war and gained control of most of New England.

By the mid-1700s, settlers moved as far west as the Ohio River valley—a region claimed by both France and Great Britain.

The victory helped the British win the French and Indian War.

Notes for Home: Your child learned about the causes and effects of the French and Indian War.
Home Activity: To practice this skill with your child, identify several cause-and-effect relationships around your home.

Vocabulary Review

Directions: Use the clues from the chapter to complete the crossword puzzle.

hacienda

presidio

El Camino Real

Pueblo Revolt

trading post

tributary

King Philip's War

backcountry

French and Indian War

Pontiac's Rebellion

Proclamation of 1763

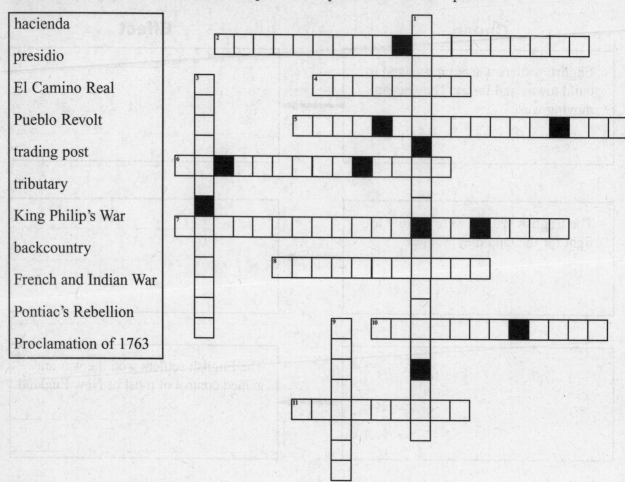

Across

2. an Ottawa leader led Native Americans in this battle against the British
4. large estate
5. war between English and Wampanoag leader, Metacom
6. road connecting Mexico City and Santa Fe
7. official document stating that colonists were not allowed to settle west of the Appalachian Mountains
8. rugged stretch of land near the Appalachian Mountains
10. place where French and Native Americans exchanged goods
11. stream or river that flows into a larger river

Down

1. battle fought between British and French in America
3. conflict between the Pueblo and the Spanish that ended in the Spanish being driven out of New Mexico
9. military fort

Notes for Home: Your child learned about struggles for control of lands in North America.
Home Activity: With your child, research one or more of the Native American groups mentioned and discuss the main struggle it faced.

Name _____ Date _____

UNIT
3 Project Colonial Living

Use with Page 258.

Directions: In a game show, see if your classmates can guess your colonial occupation. Then try to guess the other students' occupations.

1. My occupation is _____.

2. Clues about my colonial occupation (in sentence form):

     A. _____

     B. _____

     C. _____

     D. _____

     E. _____

3. Questions to ask other students to identify their colonial occupations:

_____

_____

_____

_____

_____

_____

✔Checklist for Students

_____ I chose an occupation from colonial times.

_____ I researched five statements of fact as clues about my occupation and wrote them on an index card.

_____ I wrote questions to guess other colonial occupations.

_____ I participated in the class game show.

 Notes for Home: Your child learned about occupations in colonial America.
Home Activity: Review the Fact File list of colonial occupations in Unit 3 of your child's textbook. Together, identify jobs available today that did not exist hundreds of years ago.

Name _____ Date _____

Cause and Effect

Sometimes writers use clue words such as *because, so,* or *since* to signal cause and effect. A cause may have more than one effect, and an effect may have more than one cause.

Directions: Read the following passage. Use the reading strategy of cause and effect to answer the questions. Fill in the circle next to the correct answer.

The American Revolution at Sea

Many of the battles fought during the American Revolution were fought on land, but battles were also fought at sea. The British controlled the seas. They were expected to defeat the colonists since they had a large naval fleet and the colonies did not. In the colonies, ships from the Continental Navy, along with ships from the colonies' own navy, managed to capture or sink a number of British ships. They were able to do this because they had the help of private ships, known as privateers.

The number of privateers grew during the years of the revolution, so these ships were able to cause significant damage to the British fleet. Because the privateers were spread out in the Atlantic as far as the West Indies and British Isles, their actions also hurt Britain by affecting its trade.

In 1778 the French and the American colonies formed an alliance, and Spain entered the war as an ally of France. Because of this alliance, Britain could no longer control the seas. A British fleet was always kept on guard against invasion in the English Channel. This left vast areas unguarded, so the Spanish and French naval forces were able to attack wherever they pleased.

---

1. What caused people to expect the British to defeat the colonists at sea?
   - Ⓐ Britain's allies
   - Ⓑ Britain's wealth
   - Ⓒ Britain's large navy
   - Ⓓ King George's political influence

2. What effect did the privateers have on the British fleet?
   - Ⓐ They were in the way of the Continental Navy.
   - Ⓑ They helped defeat the Continental Navy.
   - Ⓒ They helped defeat the British fleet.
   - Ⓓ They grew to the size of the British fleet.

3. What effect did Spain's and France's alliances with the American colonies have on the British?
   - Ⓐ It made them stronger.
   - Ⓑ It made them lose control of the seas.
   - Ⓒ It gave them more allies.
   - Ⓓ It expanded their naval fleet.

Notes for Home: Your child learned to apply the reading strategy of cause and effect to a passage.
Home Activity: With your child, read a newspaper article or editorial and list the causes and effects that you find.

Vocabulary Preview

Directions: Match each vocabulary word to its meaning. Write the vocabulary word on the line provided. Not all words will be used. You may use your glossary.

Parliament	Daughters of Liberty	Loyalist
Stamp Act	Boston Massacre	First Continental Congress
repeal	Committee of Correspondence	militia
Sons of Liberty	Tea Act	minutemen
Townshend Acts	Boston Tea Party	American Revolution
tariff	Intolerable Acts	Battle of Bunker Hill
boycott	Patriot	

1. _____ laws calling for a tax on imported goods

2. _____ a tax on imported goods

3. _____ law that placed a tax on printed materials in the colonies

4. _____ to cancel

5. _____ a colonist who opposed British rule

6. _____ important revolutionary battle that took place on Breed's Hill

7. _____ law that allowed only one company to sell tea to the colonists

8. _____ new laws dictated by Britain to punish the colonists for the Boston Tea Party

9. _____ group that led protests against the new Stamp Act tax

10. _____ a volunteer army

11. _____ Britain's law-making assembly

12. _____ militia groups who could be ready to fight for their colony at only a minute's notice

13. _____ a war Americans fought for independence

14. _____ when colonists dumped tea into Boston Harbor to protest the Tea Act

---

Notes for Home: Your child learned about troubles between the British and the colonies.
Home Activity: Have your child write each vocabulary word on the front of a small piece of paper and the definition on the back. Lay out these cards with the vocabulary terms face up. Then make a second set with definitions only. Lay out these cards face up. Have your child match each term with its definition.

Lesson 1: Trouble over Taxes

Directions: Match each cause to its effect to complete each sentence. Then circle the clue words that signal cause and effect.

CAUSE	EFFECT
1. Britain needed money to help cover the cost of defending the colonies,	a. so they sent warships to the colonies.
2. Since they had not voted for Parliament,	b. Britain repealed the Stamp Act.
3. Because the colonies were beginning to rebel against British taxes,	c. the colonists didn't think it was fair for Britain to tax them.
4. Britain still needed money,	d. so it decided to tax the colonists.
5. Because they didn't want to pay the tax,	e. so King George III decided to find another tax for the colonists.
6. The British wanted to convince the colonists to stop protesting the tax,	f. the colonists decided to boycott imported goods from Britain.

Directions: Read the actions of the British. Write the effect of each in the space provided.

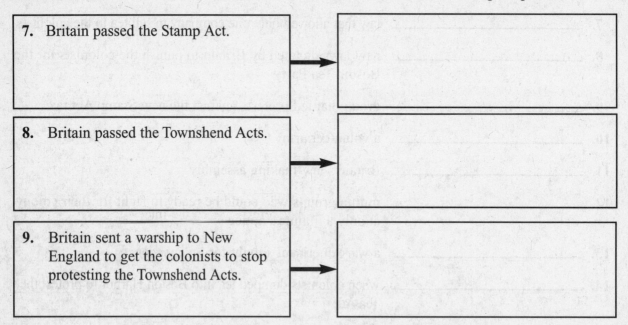

7. Britain passed the Stamp Act.

8. Britain passed the Townshend Acts.

9. Britain sent a warship to New England to get the colonists to stop protesting the Townshend Acts.

Notes for Home: Your child learned about the colonists' refusal to pay British taxes.
Home Activity: With your child, make your own cause-and-effect chart reflecting real or possible events in your personal lives.

Lesson 2: The Colonists Rebel

Directions: Answer the questions below on the lines provided. You may use your textbook.

1. What was the Boston Massacre?

   _____

   _____

2. Why did Parliament repeal the Townshend Acts?

   _____

   _____

3. Why did Parliament decide to keep the tax on tea?

   _____

   _____

4. Who was Paul Revere?

   _____

   _____

5. What two goals did the British hope to accomplish by passing the Tea Act?

   _____

   _____

6. How did the colonists respond to the Tea Act?

   _____

   _____

7. Why did Britain pass new laws that the colonists referred to as the Intolerable Acts?

   _____

   _____

Notes for Home: Your child learned why the colonists protested British taxation.
Home Activity: With your child, discuss this lesson. Then have your child write the main idea of the lesson on a large self-stick note. Have him or her write supporting details on smaller self-stick notes and place them around the perimeter of the main-idea note.

Use Primary Sources

Primary sources are eyewitness accounts of history. They give you firsthand knowledge about how things were at the time of the event. They are made by people who participated in the event being described. Primary sources can be letters, diaries, documents, speeches, interviews, photographs, paintings, or newspapers. Many of the pictures in this chapter of your textbook are photographs of primary sources.

Directions: The primary source below relates to the Boston Massacre. Study the source and answer the questions that follow.

1. What is taking place in this picture?

   _____

   _____

2. Why do you think the incident was referred to as a "massacre"? What does this picture tell you about how the British soldiers responded to colonists who protested during revolutionary times?

   _____

   _____

Notes for Home: Your child learned to identify and study primary sources.
Home Activity: With your child, examine postcards or letters from family or friends. Describe what about the wording identifies the item as a primary source. Then identify the person's perspective on the events being described.

Name _____ Date _____

Lesson 3: The Revolution Begins

Directions: Complete the sequence chart by writing the sentences in the box in the order in which they took place. You may use your textbook.

- British soldiers secretly begin marching from Boston to Concord.
- British soldiers suffer heavy losses from Patriots firing at them as they walk the 20 miles from Concord to safety in Boston.
- Colonel Prescott's men work all night building a fort to defend Breed's Hill.
- Paul Revere knows of the British soldiers' plan and sets out to warn the militias in Lexington and Concord.
- The British win the Battle of Lexington.
- The British suffer heavy losses but win the Battle of Bunker Hill.
- The shot known as "the shot heard round the world" is fired.

1.

2.

3.

4.

5.

6.

7.

 Notes for Home: Your child learned the events that led to the American Revolution.
Home Activity: Discuss with your child ways countries can try to resolve conflicts without going to war.

Vocabulary Review

Directions: Choose the vocabulary term from the box that best completes each sentence. Not all words will be used. Write the term on the line provided.

Parliament	Daughters of Liberty	Loyalist
Stamp Act	Boston Massacre	First Continental Congress
repeal	Committee of Correspondence	militia
Sons of Liberty	Tea Act	minutemen
Townshend Acts	Boston Tea Party	American Revolution
tariff	Intolerable Acts	Battle of Bunker Hill
boycott	Patriot	

1. The government decided to _____, or cancel, the law.

2. Local merchants held a _____ against imported goods.

3. The _____ were laws punishing the colonists for dumping tea into Boston Harbor.

4. Even today, _____ continues to be the law-making assembly for Great Britain.

5. The _____ required all colonists to pay a tax on printed materials.

6. The _____ was formed by representatives of all but one of the 13 colonies. Representatives voted on what action to take against the British and their taxes.

7. The _____ were laws requiring a tax be paid on imported goods.

8. The killing of five men in Boston by panicked British soldiers is known as the

_____ .

9. The British lost many soldiers in the _____, which actually took place on Breed's Hill.

10. The _____ supported the boycott of imported goods by making tea from herbs and berries and by weaving cloth.

Notes for Home: Your child learned about how the American Revolution began.
Home Activity: Have your child draw a picture representing the American Revolution period and have him or her explain the picture using as many vocabulary words as possible.

Vocabulary Preview

Directions: Find the meaning of each vocabulary term from Chapter 9. Write the meaning on the lines provided. You may use your glossary.

Second Continental Congress _____

_____

Continental Army _____

_____

Olive Branch Petition _____

_____

Declaration of Independence _____

_____

traitor _____

_____

Green Mountain Boys _____

_____

mercenary _____

_____

Battle of Saratoga _____

_____

Treaty of Paris _____

_____

_____

Notes for Home: Your child learned about the American Revolution.
Home Activity: Help your child learn the terms and their meanings by using each term in a sentence.

Lesson 1: Declaring Independence

Directions: Put the events in the sequence chart in the correct order. Number the events from 1 (earliest) to 10 (latest). Write the numbers on the blank lines before the boxes.

_____ | Thomas Paine publishes *Common Sense*.

_____ | Congress attempts to avoid war by sending a petition to King George III.

_____ | The Continental Army is formed.

_____ | George Washington agrees to command the army.

_____ | The Declaration of Independence is signed by the members of Congress.

_____ | King George wants to "put a speedy end" to the illegal rebellion in the colonies.

_____ | The Second Continental Congress is held.

_____ | Congress decides to vote for independence.

Notes for Home: Your child learned about Congress's decision to declare independence.
Home Activity: With your child, write a cause and effect for each event in this lesson on a separate slip of paper. Cut apart each cause and effect. Mix up the slips of paper and have your child put them back in the correct sequence.

Lesson 2: Patriots at War

Directions: Answer the questions on the lines provided. You may use your textbook.

1. How did winning the Battle of Fort Ticonderoga help the Patriots later in the war?

_____

_____

_____

2. Why did the British hire mercenaries to fight the war?

_____

_____

3. How did the American victory at Trenton affect Americans?

_____

_____

_____

4. How did winning the Battle of Saratoga affect the remainder of the war?

_____

_____

_____

_____

5. Why did African American Patriots fight in the war?

_____

_____

Critical Thinking: Who said, "I only regret that I have but one life to lose for my country"? Explain this quote.

_____

_____

Notes for Home: Your child learned about people who contributed to the American Revolution.
Home Activity: Ask your child to explain why it was important for individual colonists to contribute to the war effort. Have him or her show you examples of these brave Patriots in the text.

Lesson 3: The World Turned Upside Down

Use with Pages 314–319.

Directions: Identify the cause and effect in each row. Label each item "Cause" or "Effect" in the space provided. Then draw an arrow between the boxes to show which event led to the other. The first one has been done for you.

1. Cause	Effect
New soldiers and food arrive at Valley Forge. Von Steuben, a German officer, trains Washington's men.	American soldiers turn into a stronger, professional army.

2.	
France and Spain join the Americans in the war against Britain.	The American war effort receives more ships, soldiers, and money.

3.	
Spanish victories weaken British power in what is now the Southeast region of the United States.	Spanish troops from Spanish Louisiana capture British forts along the Mississippi River and Gulf of Mexico.

4.	
The British capture Savannah, Georgia.	The British are unable to defeat the Americans in the North and try a new strategy, hoping to find more Loyalists.

5.	
Patriots such as Francis Marion, known as the Swamp Fox, and Nathanael Greene use unconventional tactics against the British.	The British grow frustrated and tired and change their strategy.

6.	
Cornwallis surrenders his army to Washington.	The Americans and the French surround the British at Yorktown.

7.	
The Treaty of Paris is signed.	Great Britain recognizes the United States of America as an independent nation.

Notes for Home: Your child learned to identify causes and effects.
Home Activity: Explain to your child that sometimes cause-and-effect relationships are worded as "if … then …" statements. Together, change each of the cause-and-effect relationships in the lesson to an "if … then …" statement.

Make Generalizations

A generalization is a broad statement or idea about a subject. It explains how different facts might have an important idea in common. Generalizations help explain the big picture and make it easier to remember many different facts.

Directions: Read the following passage and answer the questions on the lines provided.

The American Revolution was a long-lasting and difficult battle for independence. Although this war often is portrayed as being fought entirely by men, this is not true. Women contributed to the war effort in a number of ways.

The struggle for independence was not limited to battles on the battlefield. It included caring for the soldiers as well as providing funding to keep the effort going. For a time, Washington's army struggled because it had insufficient food and inadequate clothing for protection from the elements. George Washington's wife, Martha, and many other women prepared food for the soldiers and cared for the wounded.

These patriotic women reasoned that independence was for everybody, not just for the soldiers. Martha Washington and other women sewed and mended the soldiers' clothing. They also knitted socks for the soldiers, who often had gone barefoot in battle and in the snow, risking their health and their lives.

History also tells of women participating on the battlefield. One story tells of a woman who joined the army under a man's name. She fought in numerous battles and was wounded twice before her secret was revealed. Another woman reportedly took her husband's place in battle after his death.

Published writings also helped support the war effort. Women wrote and published songs and other works in an effort to boost soldiers' morale and increase public awareness. The better informed people were, the more likely they were to support the war effort with money and various types of volunteer service.

1. Which sentence tells you the main idea of the passage? _____

_____

2. Which sentence in the passage is a generalization? _____

_____

3. What generalization can you make about the passage? _____

_____

Notes for Home: Your child learned how to make generalizations.
Home Activity: With your child, practice making both true and false generalizations about events in your daily lives. Discuss what types of mistakes lead to false generalizations.

Name _____ Date _____

Vocabulary Review

Directions: Match each vocabulary term from Chapter 9 to its cause, clue, or definition. Write the term in the space provided.

Second Continental Congress	Declaration of Independence	mercenary
Continental Army	traitor	Battle of Saratoga
Olive Branch Petition	Green Mountain Boys	Treaty of Paris

1. _____ Great Britain recognizes the United States of America as an independent nation.

2. _____ Colonial militias clashing with British soldiers at Concord and Lexington cause American leaders to meet and make many decisions.

3. _____ Determined to win the war against the Americans, King George hires German soldiers to fight for Britain.

4. _____ This was necessary for America to defend itself against the British army.

5. _____ Britain attempts to take control of Lake Champlain and the Hudson River.

6. _____ Congress prepares a document in an effort to gain every colony's support. The document explains the Americans' reasons for breaking with Britain.

7. _____ This was a group of Patriot soldiers from Vermont, led by Ethan Allen.

8. _____ Congress offers a peaceful solution to the problem with Britain.

9. _____ Benedict Arnold fights for the British in exchange for money.

Notes for Home: Your child learned about events of the American Revolution.
Home Activity: With your child, examine each of the given causes, clues, and definitions and underline key words. Encourage your child to use these key words to remember the meanings of the chapter 9 vocabulary terms.

Name _____   Date _____

UNIT
4 Project   News Then

Use with Page 328.

Directions: In a group, present a news program about an event described in this unit from the 1760s or during the American Revolution. Group members should choose a role and complete the assignment for that role.

1. The event is _____.

2. My role in the news program is (✔ one):

   ____ News anchor   ____ Reporter   ____ Eyewitness

3. News Anchor
   Write a summary of the event. Describe the people involved, details about their role, and the outcome or importance of the event.

   _____

   _____

4. Reporter
   Write questions (and answers) on behalf of the eyewitnesses to the event. Ask them who was involved, what the people did, and what they think is the outcome or importance of the event.

   _____

   _____

5. Eyewitness
   If you are an eyewitness, write a description of what you saw. Include the names of the people involved, what they did, and the outcome or importance of the event.

   _____

   _____

✔ **Checklist for Students**

_____ We chose an event from the 1760s or the American Revolution.
_____ We each chose a role to play in the news program.
_____ We wrote about the event from the point of view of our assigned role.
_____ Our group made a banner and background for our news program.

Notes for Home: Your child learned about events of the late 1700s.
Home Activity: With your child, watch a news program about national events. Discuss the roles reporters, news anchors, and eyewitnesses play in sharing a news event with TV viewers.

Draw Conclusions

Directions: Read the information below. Then fill in the circle next to the correct answer.

The French Revolution took place at about the same time as the American Revolution. Both countries were trying to achieve a democratic form of government. One major difference, however, was that the French already had a government in place.

During the course of the French Revolution, the existing French government would be completely destroyed. The majority of French citizens were dissatisfied with it and would not rest until it was changed.

At that time, the French government was led by a king, and citizens belonged to different social classes. Benefits and privileges were given to some according to their social class. For instance, some classes did not have to pay taxes and were allowed to collect dues from the poorer classes.

Another factor leading to the French Revolution was a lack of money. France had just helped the United States battle Britain in the American Revolution, and now it needed money. France already taxed some of its people, but now the situation called for additional taxes. Representatives of the king decided to begin taxing *all* landowners. This unpopular action caused the people to rebel against their government and resist what they considered to be unfair treatment.

Violent protests took place throughout the country. Poorer citizens fought for their own rights and to keep the wealthy from receiving special privileges.

Before the end of the French Revolution, the existing social divisions were outlawed. However, France's problems were far from over.

1. Which statement supports the conclusion that the American Revolution helped spark the French Revolution?

   Ⓐ The French government was ruled by a king.

   Ⓑ French citizens belonged to different social classes.

   Ⓒ France had just helped the Americans battle Britain in the American Revolution.

   Ⓓ There was a great deal of civil unrest in France.

2. Which statement supports the conclusion that the majority of French people wanted a new form of government?

   Ⓐ Poorer citizens fought for their rights and to keep the wealthy from receiving special privileges.

   Ⓑ Money was one cause of the French Revolution.

   Ⓒ Privileges were determined by social class.

   Ⓓ France already taxed some of its people.

Notes for Home: Your child learned how to draw conclusions about a historical event.
Home Activity: With your child, brainstorm a list of facts about the American Revolution and another list of facts about the French Revolution. Together, draw conclusions about how the Americans may have influenced the French citizenry to rebel against their government.

Vocabulary Preview

Directions: Match each vocabulary term to its definition. Write the number of the term in the space provided. Not all terms will be used. You may use your glossary.

1. Articles of Confederation
2. ratify
3. legislative branch
4. executive branch
5. judicial branch
6. inflation
7. Shays' Rebellion
8. Northwest Ordinance
9. delegate
10. Constitutional Convention
11. Virginia Plan
12. New Jersey Plan
13. compromise
14. Great Compromise
15. Three-Fifths Compromise
16. Preamble
17. reserved powers
18. separation of powers
19. checks and balances
20. veto
21. Federalists
22. federal
23. Antifederalists
24. *The Federalist*
25. amendment
26. Bill of Rights

___ **a.** to approve something

___ **b.** system to guard against any one branch of the government becoming too powerful

___ **c.** movement by farmers to protest high taxes

___ **d.** a representative

___ **e.** plan that proposed that each state, regardless of size, would have the same number of representatives in Congress

___ **f.** an addition or change to the Constitution

___ **g.** happens when prices rise very quickly

___ **h.** each side gives up something to reach an agreement

___ **i.** three out of every five slaves would be counted for population and taxation

___ **j.** group of people who were not happy with the Constitution

___ **k.** assembly that replaced the Articles of Confederation

___ **l.** the part of the government that passes laws

___ **m.** formerly nationalist group that wanted a strong national government

___ **n.** plan that proposed that Congress should be given much greater power over the states

___ **o.** the part of the government that carries out laws

___ **p.** each branch of the government has different and separate powers

___ **q.** plan for national government where states would keep their freedom and independence

___ **r.** to refuse to sign into law

___ **s.** an order that commanded that the Northwest Territory be divided into smaller territories

___ **t.** refers to the national government

Notes for Home: Your child learned about the formation of a new government for the United States.
Home Activity: Write each vocabulary word or its definition on a blank index card. Then read each card to your child, having him or her provide the missing word or definition.

Lesson 1: A Weak Government

Directions: Complete the following fact-and-conclusion chart. In each box at left, write one fact to support the conclusion. You may use your textbook.

Facts

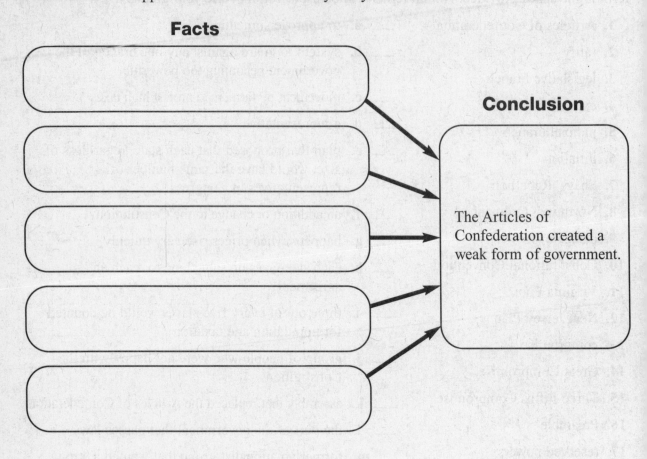

Conclusion

The Articles of Confederation created a weak form of government.

Directions: The United States needed money to repay the individuals and the countries who had loaned money for the American Revolution. The United States also needed to pay the soldiers who had fought in the war. Do you think Daniel Shays and others like him who fought in the war should have been taxed to pay the country's war debts? Explain.

_____

_____

_____

_____

Notes for Home: Your child learned about problems in the government of the United States under the Articles of Confederation.
Home Activity: With your child, review this lesson and list facts and any conclusions that can be drawn.

Lesson 2: Debate in Philadelphia

Directions: Describe each of the following three terms in your own words. Relate each term to at least one of the other terms. Finally, answer question 4. You may use your textbook.

1. Constitutional Convention

_____

_____

_____

_____

2. Virginia Plan

_____

_____

_____

_____

_____

_____

3. Great Compromise

_____

_____

_____

_____

4. Why was a government with three branches considered to be a compromise?

_____

_____

_____

_____

Notes for Home: Your child learned about the creation of the United States Constitution.
Home Activity: With your child, talk about an event in your child's life when he or she had to compromise.

Lesson 3: Ratifying the Constitution

Directions: A flowchart is a diagram that shows, step by step, a process of how something works or happens. Complete the flowchart using the items in the box.

Antifederalists	*The Federalist* essays explained the weaknesses of Antifederalist arguments.
A Bill of Rights is promised.	All 13 states ratify the Constitution, making it the supreme law of the land.
Federalists	This group feared that the central government would pass laws that were not suitable for all parts of the country.

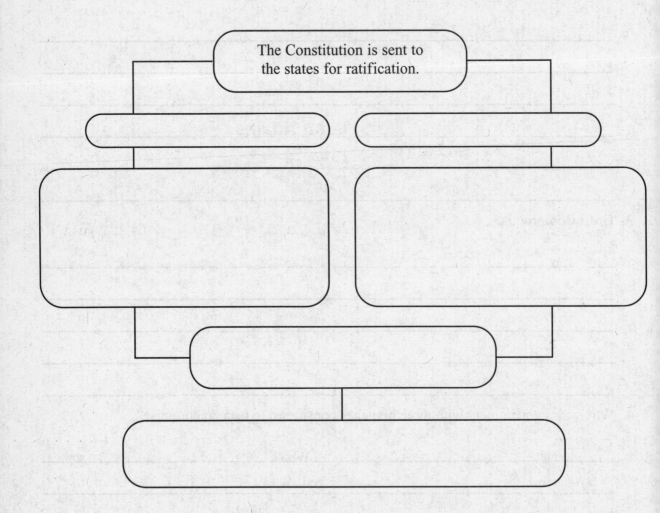

The Constitution is sent to the states for ratification.

Gather and Report Information

Suppose you were going to write a report on the first Vice-President of the United States. Think of the information you would need to write your report.

Directions: Read the information about gathering and reporting information. Answer the questions that follow.

1. An encyclopedia has the following entries. Which one will you need?

   Ⓐ Adams, John (1735–1826) Second President of the United States
   Ⓑ Adams, John Couch (1819–1892) English astronomer
   Ⓒ Adams, John Quincy (1767–1848) Sixth President of the United States
   Ⓓ Adams, Samuel (1722–1803) Signer of the Declaration of Independence

2. Explain the reasoning behind your answer to question 1.

   _____

   _____

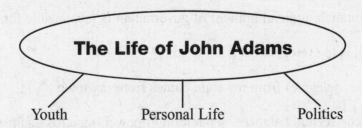

The Life of John Adams

Youth   Personal Life   Politics

3. What is the subject of the report outlined in the graphic organizer above? Explain your

   reasoning. _____

   _____

4. An encyclopedia article on John Adams has the following subheadings. Which might be most useful for your report?

   Ⓐ Political Opponents
   Ⓑ U.S.S. John Adams
   Ⓒ Boyhood and Education
   Ⓓ The John Adams Institute

5. An Internet search reveals the following sources. Which one do you think is a primary source?

   Ⓐ Adams, John, *The Adams Papers*, 13 vols., ed. by Lyman H. Butterfield et al. (1961–77)
   Ⓑ Ferling, John, *John Adams: A Life* (1992)
   Ⓒ Kurtz, Stephen G., *The Presidency of John Adams* (1957)
   Ⓓ Shaw, Peter, *The Character of John Adams* (1976)

Notes for Home: Your child learned how to gather and report information.
Home Activity: With your child, discuss where he or she might research information for a report. Together, analyze what types of information might be found in the library, in an encyclopedia, or on the Internet.

Vocabulary Review

Directions: Circle the vocabulary term that best completes each sentence. Not all terms will be used.

Articles of Confederation	Constitutional Convention	checks and balances
ratify	Virginia Plan	veto
legislative branch	New Jersey Plan	Federalists
executive branch	compromise	federal
judicial branch	Great Compromise	Antifederalists
inflation	Three-Fifths Compromise	*The Federalist*
Shays' Rebellion	Preamble	amendment
Northwest Ordinance	reserved powers	Bill of Rights
delegate	separation of powers	

1. The (legislative branch, judicial branch) of government is responsible for the court system.

2. To approve a bill is to (veto, ratify) it.

3. The (compromise, delegate) from my state comes from my town.

4. The system of (checks and balances, separation of powers) guards against any one branch of the government becoming too powerful.

5. (Compromise, Inflation) happens when prices rise very quickly.

6. An addition or change is known as a(n) (amendment, veto).

7. The (Northwest Ordinance, Articles of Confederation) turned out to be a plan of government that was too weak in many people's opinions.

8. In a (compromise, constitution), each side gives up something to reach an agreement.

9. The (Three-Fifths Compromise, Bill of Rights) is a group of ten amendments to the Constitution.

10. The word (*federal, inflation*) refers to the national government.

11. (Reserved powers, Checks and balances) are powers left strictly to state governments.

12. The (Federalists, Antifederalists) were a group that wanted a strong national government.

Notes for Home: Your child learned how the United States struggled to find a suitable form of government.
Home Activity: With your child, study the vocabulary definitions by playing a question-and-answer game. First, read your child a definition. Then have him or her give the answer in question form, such as "What are the Articles of Confederation?"

Vocabulary Preview

Directions: Choose the vocabulary term from the box that best completes each sentence. Not all terms will be used. Write the word on the line provided. You may use your glossary.

electoral college	pioneer	neutral	War of 1812
inauguration	frontier	Battle of Tippecanoe	national anthem
Cabinet	Louisiana Purchase	War Hawks	Battle of New Orleans
political party			

1. The _____ doubled the size of the United States.

2. "The Star-Spangled Banner" is the _____ of the United States.

3. The _____ is made up of people chosen by each state to vote for the President and Vice-President.

4. Daniel Boone was a _____, or person who pushed westward searching for land to settle.

5. To remain _____ is not to take sides.

6. A _____ is an organized group of people who share a view of what government should be and do.

7. The _____ was fought in the present-day state of Indiana between United States forces and Tecumseh's soldiers.

8. The _____ took place after the official end to the War of 1812 because the news had not yet arrived from Europe.

9. The _____ is remembered for dramatic battles at sea.

10. _____ is the ceremony when a newly elected President swears loyalty to the Constitution and takes office.

11. The _____ is the edge of settlement for early settlers who pushed westward.

12. Members of Congress who pressed for war against Britain were known as

_____.

Notes for Home: Your child learned about the first struggles in our new nation.
Home Activity: With your child, practice spelling and defining the vocabulary words by creating a puzzle or writing each term in an original sentence.

Lesson 1: Washington as President

Directions: Match each name in the box to its description. Write the name on the line provided. Names may be used more than once.

George Washington	Thomas Jefferson	Benjamin Banneker
Alexander Hamilton	Pierre L'Enfant	John Adams

1. _____ He had plans to set up a national bank.

2. _____ He was elected President by the electoral college in a unanimous vote.

3. _____ He was the secretary of state under Washington.

4. _____ He was a member of the Democratic-Republican party.

5. _____ He was the secretary of the treasury under Washington.

6. _____ He designed the city of Washington, D.C.

7. _____ He opposed setting up a national bank.

8. _____ He was the first President to live in the President's House.

9. _____ Originally, he didn't want to become President.

10. _____ He was the second President of the United States.

11. _____ He believed in a strong national government.

12. _____ He was an astronomer who helped survey the land where Washington, D.C., was built.

13. _____ He was a member of the Federalist political party.

14. _____ He wanted the country to remain a land of small farmers and skilled crafts workers.

15. _____ He was "First in war, first in peace, and first in the hearts of his countrymen."

Notes for Home: Your child learned about events that took place under President George Washington and Vice-President John Adams.
Home Activity: With your child, talk about how the U.S. government would be different today if two political parties had not developed.

Lesson 2: Jefferson Looks West

Directions: Complete each sentence with information from Lesson 2. You may use your textbook.

1. Thomas Jefferson was the _____ President of the United States.

2. Jefferson believed that the power of government belonged in the hands of the

   _____.

3. In search of new lands to settle, Americans began moving _____

   long before Jefferson became President.

4. Daniel Boone, an early pioneer, created the trail known as the

   _____.

5. Boone led many pioneers through the _____, across the

   Appalachian Mountains.

6. Settlers along the Ohio and Mississippi Rivers used these waterways as

   _____ routes to ship their products south.

7. Goods shipped along the Mississippi went to the Spanish-controlled port of

   _____ and then to the East Coast and Europe.

8. The United States doubled in size with the _____, acquiring land

   that stretched from the Mississippi River to the Rocky Mountains.

9. Jefferson was interested in the lands to the west and chose _____

   to head an expedition to explore the unknown area.

10. The expedition to explore the West included the help of a French trapper and his Shoshone

    wife, _____, who served as a guide and interpreter for the expedition.

Notes for Home: Your child learned about changes in the nation under President Thomas Jefferson.
Home Activity: With your child, examine a map of the United States and list the present-day states that would not be part of the United States if not for the Louisiana Purchase and the Lewis and Clark expedition.

Compare Population Density Maps

Population density maps show how many people live in an area. Comparing population density maps of the same area from different time periods can show how the population changed over time. In the maps below, each dot represents 200 enslaved persons.

Directions: Study the maps. Answer the questions that follow in the spaces provided.

Map A: 1790

Map B: 1830

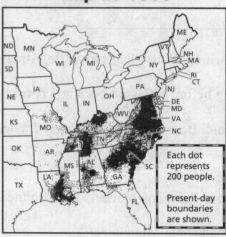

1. According to Map A, which state had the greatest number of enslaved persons in 1790?

_____

2. According to Map B, which two states had the greatest number of enslaved persons in 1830?

_____

3. According to Map B, was the population of enslaved persons in 1830 more dense in Northern states or in Southern states?

_____

4. According to Map A, which of the following states had the lowest population of enslaved persons in 1790? Circle the correct answer.

   Virginia   Maryland   Pennsylvania

5. According to the two maps, how did the population of enslaved persons in Kentucky change from 1790 to 1830?

_____

_____

Notes for Home: Your child learned to read population density maps.
Home Activity: Using the maps on this page, discuss with your child possible reasons for the increase in the population of enslaved persons in the United States between 1790 and 1830.

Lesson 3: Another War with Britain

Directions: Read each pair of cause-and-effect statements. Label each statement
Cause or *Effect* in the space provided. Draw an arrow from the cause to the effect.

1. France and Britain are at war. Neither wants the other to receive supplies from the United States.	Both France and Britain interfere with U.S. shipping.
2. U.S. trade with other countries is almost completely cut off.	The British Navy seizes U.S. sailors and cargo.
3. The Battle of Tippecanoe between U.S. forces and Native Americans is led by Shawnee leader Tecumseh.	Shawnee leader Tecumseh unites Native Americans to resist the settlement of pioneers.
4. The United States wants to end British-supported attacks against settlers on the frontier and to take Canada from the British.	America declares war on Britain. The War of 1812 lasts for two and one-half years.
5. The American warship *Constitution* receives the nickname "Old Ironsides."	In a battle between the United States and the British off the east coast of Canada, British cannonballs seem to bounce off the sides of the American warship *Constitution*.

Directions: Answer the following question in the space provided.

What is one unfulfilled American expectation of the War of 1812?

_____

_____

Notes for Home: Your child learned about why the United States went to war with Britain in 1812.
Home Activity: With your child, discuss how things might be different today if the United States still had
an adversarial relationship with Britain. Ask whether he or she thinks the United States and Britain will ever
declare war with each other in the future. Why or why not?

Vocabulary Review

Directions: Complete the crossword puzzle using the clues below and the vocabulary words from Chapter 11.

Across

1. An early settler who moved westward

4. A _____ party is an organized group of people who share a view of what government should be and do.

5. This ceremony is held when a newly elected President swears loyalty to the Constitution and takes office.

9. Agreement that doubled the size of the United States with land bought from the French

10. The _____ of 1812 is remembered for dramatic battles at sea.

11. The heads of certain government departments are known as this. These heads advise and help the President.

12. The official song of the United States is its national _____.

13. The _____ college is made up of people chosen by each state to vote for the President and Vice-President.

Down

2. The Battle of _____ took place after a treaty ending the war had been signed in Europe.

3. The edge of settlement for those who pushed westward

6. Not taking sides

7. The Battle of _____ was fought in the present-day state of Indiana between U.S. forces and Tecumseh's soldiers.

8. Members of Congress who pressed for war against Britain were known as War _____.

Notes for Home: Your child learned about developments in the United States during the first presidency and thereafter.
Home Activity: With your child, create a word-search puzzle using the vocabulary terms. Create clues from the words' definitions.

5 Project   Two Sides

Use with Page 392.

Directions: In a group, use your textbook and other references to research questions and answers for all roles. Then hold a press conference about the ratification of the Bill of Rights.

1. Questions a news reporter might ask a Federalist:

_____

_____

2. A Federalist's answers:

_____

_____

3. Questions a news reporter might ask an Antifederalist:

_____

_____

4. An Antifederalist's answers:

_____

_____

5. In the press conference, my role is (✔ one):

___ Federalist   ___ Antifederalist   ___ News reporter

6. My argument (✔ one) for ___ or against ___ ratifying the Bill of Rights is _____

_____

✔ Checklist for Students

_____ I wrote my arguments for or against ratifying the Bill of Rights.

_____ I wrote questions and answers on behalf of the news reporter, Federalists, and Antifederalists.

_____ I chose a role to play in the press conference.

_____ I helped stage the classroom press coverage.

Notes for Home: Your child learned how Federalists and Antifederalists viewed the Bill of Rights.
Home Activity: With your child, discuss the importance of listening to opposing points of view. Give personal examples.

Compare and Contrast

Learning how to compare and contrast information will help you better understand similarities and differences. To compare, writers often use clue words such as *both, as,* or *like*. To contrast, words such as *unlike, in contrast,* or *different* may be used.

Directions: Fill in the circle next to the correct answer.

The role of women and women's rights have changed dramatically over the course of many years. In the early 1800s, women had few rights in contrast to men. Women and men were not considered equals.

Unlike men, women were not allowed to vote, and any property owned by a single woman became the property of her husband as soon as they were married.

During the American Revolution both men and women supported the war in the name of liberty and equality. Although the end of the war did not bring a change to women's rights, the idea of equality grew stronger.

The Industrial Revolution affected the role of women in society and women's rights in general. One difference resulting from the Industrial Revolution was that women had the chance to work away from home. Working-class women also now had the opportunity to earn a wage, which belonged to the husband if she was married.

In 1848 the Seneca Falls Convention was held in honor of women's rights. It declared that women and men should be considered as equals. Other changes to women's rights also took place around the same time. Some states enacted laws allowing married women, like men, to own property; to control their own earnings; and to have joint custody of their children.

---

1. Which of the following was a right shared by both men and women as a result of the Industrial Revolution?

   Ⓐ Men and women worked away from home.
   Ⓑ Men and women owned property.
   Ⓒ Men and women voted.
   Ⓓ Men and women had equal custody of their children.

2. What right had women gained by the 1850s?

   Ⓐ the right to full custody of their children
   Ⓑ the right to vote
   Ⓒ the right to own property
   Ⓓ the right to fight in battle

Notes for Home: Your child learned how to compare and contrast written information.
Home Activity: With your child, draw a chart comparing and contrasting information in a newspaper article of interest.

Vocabulary Preview

Directions: Match each vocabulary term to its definition. Write the term in the space provided. Not all words will be used.

nationalism	Industrial Revolution	reform
Era of Good Feelings	manufacture	revival
Monroe Doctrine	technology	temperance
suffrage	cotton gin	abolitionist
Indian Removal Act	mechanical reaper	Seneca Falls Convention
Trail of Tears	canal	

1. _____ A convention called to take a stand for women's rights

2. _____ The terrible journey forced upon the Cherokee to move to Indian Territory

3. _____ A statement that warned European nations against considering the American continents for future colonization

4. _____ A machine invented to clean the seeds out of cotton

5. _____ A reformer who attacked slavery

6. _____ A time when people began producing goods by machine rather than by hand

7. _____ Act that ordered Native Americans of the southern United States be moved west of the Mississippi River

8. _____ A time when disagreements about national issues grew quiet

9. _____ The right to vote

10. _____ The idea that all people should pull together with a sense of strong pride in their country

11. _____ Moderation

12. _____ Change

 Notes for Home: Your child learned vocabulary dealing with the mid-1800s, a time of growth and change in the United States.
Home Activity: Ask your child to use these terms to summarize the turbulent events in the United States during this time.

Lesson 1: The United States Turns Fifty

Directions: Match the events and descriptions in the box below with the President who was in office when they took place. Write each event in the space provided.

Issued warning to European nations not to consider the American continents as subject for future colonization

Headed a new political party, the Democrats

Era of Good Feelings enjoyed

Florida purchased from Spain for $5 million

Native Americans in the southern states forced to move west of the Mississippi

Known as "the man of the people"

Military leader and self-taught lawyer

Encouraged nationalism

President James Monroe	President Andrew Jackson

Critical Thinking: Compare and contrast how the United States expanded its borders under Presidents Monroe and Jackson.

_____

_____

_____

_____

Notes for Home: Your child learned about the early expansion of the United States.
Home Activity: Review the lesson with your child, and make a time line of the key events of the United States first 50 years.

Lesson 2: A New Kind of Revolution

Directions: Complete the chart by filling in the last column with one benefit of the following inventions. You may use your textbook.

Before the Invention	Invention	Benefit
There were no factories to spin cotton in the United States.	Samuel Slater built the first cotton-spinning mill in the United States.	
Cleaning seeds out of cotton was slow and difficult work.	Eli Whitney invented the cotton gin.	
Crops were harvested by hand.	Cyrus McCormick built the mechanical reaper.	
Iron plows were used to clear land.	John Deere developed the steel plow.	
Boats powered by sails or oars had difficulties traveling upstream, against the current.	Robert Fulton invented a riverboat powered by a steam engine.	
Water transportation was cheaper than land transportation, but water routes did not flow in all parts of the country.	The Erie Canal was constructed.	
Horse-drawn wagons pulled heavy loads on rough roads.	Peter Cooper built a steam-powered locomotive.	

Notes for Home: Your child learned about inventions of the Industrial Revolution.
Home Activity: Discuss inventions that help people work more quickly, more cheaply, and with less effort. What new inventions might help us in the near future?

Name _____ Date _____

Read a Cross-Section Diagram

A cross-section diagram is a drawing that shows a view of something as if you could slice through it. Cross-section diagrams can show you how something works. This cross-section diagram shows you how the cotton gin worked.

Directions: Study the diagram and answer the questions that follow.

Eli Whitney's Cotton Gin

2. Handle is turned to spin cylinder.

4. Seeds are caught in tray.

5. Brushes clean cotton bolls.

1. Fill container.

6. Clean cotton gathered.

container holds cotton bolls

3. Hooks on cylinder remove seeds.

container for cleaned cotton

1. What do the hooks do?

_____

_____

2. What is the first step in using a cotton gin?

_____

_____

3. At what step and how are cotton bolls cleaned?

_____

_____

Notes for Home: Your child learned how to read a cross-section diagram.
Home Activity: With your child, create a cross-section of a household appliance to show how it works. Use reference materials as necessary.

Lesson 3: The Struggle for Reforms

Directions: Complete the organizer with terms from the box. Write a brief description on the lines provided.

Abolitionists	Revivals
Attack on Bad Behavior	Seneca Falls Convention
Fight Against Slavery	Temperance
Religion	Women's Rights

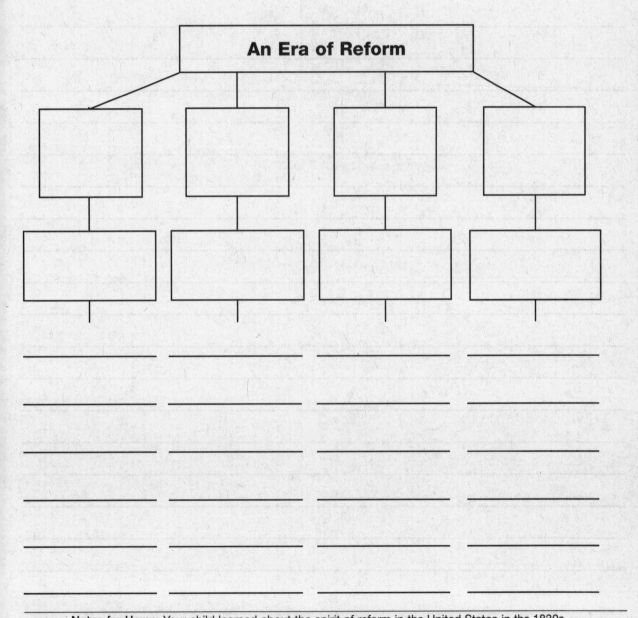

An Era of Reform

_____ _____ _____

_____ _____ _____

_____ _____ _____

_____ _____ _____

_____ _____ _____

Notes for Home: Your child learned about the spirit of reform in the United States in the 1830s.
Home Activity: With your child, discuss government's attempts to make political and social reforms in the United States today. What are the goals of these efforts to enact change?

Writing Prompt: Making Changes

Throughout the nineteenth century, reformers worked to stop child labor. Finally, in 1938 Congress passed the Fair Labor Standards Act. It set 18 as the youngest age for factory workers. Do you think children should be allowed to work? Write about reasons you agree or disagree with the reformers.

_____

_____

_____

_____

_____

_____

_____

_____

_____

_____

_____

_____

_____

_____

_____

_____

_____

_____

_____

Notes for Home: Your child learned about different reform movements.
Home Activity: With your child, discuss how life might be different today for women and African Americans if people had not worked to gain equal rights.

Vocabulary Review

Directions: Circle the term that best completes each sentence.

1. Thousands of people were forced to relocate following the terms of the (Seneca Falls Convention, Indian Removal Act).

2. A peaceful atmosphere existed in the United States during the (Era of Good Feelings, Monroe Doctrine).

3. The (cotton gin, revival) increased workers' daily production tremendously.

4. Modern (technology, reform) has created many jobs.

5. Goods were sent on the (Trail of Tears, canal) to get to market.

6. The (Monroe Doctrine, Indian Removal Act) showed foreign powers that the United States was willing to fight for its land.

7. A Wednesday evening (revival, reform) was a popular function at many houses of worship.

8. The Second Great Awakening movement supported social (temperance, reform).

9. The (Seneca Falls Convention, Industrial Revolution) introduced an era of machine-made goods.

10. Many women who supported (temperance, technology) tried to stop the drinking of alcohol.

11. The invention of machines helped businesses (manufacture, reform) goods on a wide scale.

12. Frederick Douglass, a former slave, was an outspoken (mechanical reaper, abolitionist).

13. Many people died along the (Trail of Tears, Industrial Revolution).

14. The (revival, Seneca Falls Convention) in New York supported women's rights.

15. Women and minorities had to fight for (suffrage, temperance).

16. Independence Day celebrations reflect a spirit of (reform, nationalism) in the United States.

17. The (Era of Good Feelings, mechanical reaper) made it easier for farm workers to harvest wheat.

Notes for Home: Your child learned about changes that Americans wanted to make to improve their lives.
Home Activity: Review with your child how changes in the 1800s affect our life today.

Vocabulary Preview

Directions: Define each term on the lines provided. You may use your glossary.

Texas Revolution _____

_____

annex _____

_____

manifest destiny _____

_____

Mexican War _____

_____

Bear Flag Revolt _____

_____

Treaty of Guadalupe Hidalgo _____

_____

mountain man _____

_____

wagon train _____

_____

gold rush _____

_____

forty-niner _____

_____

discrimination _____

_____

 Notes for Home: Your child learned terms related to the expansion of United States borders around 1850.
Home Activity: Have your child use these terms to tell how westward expansion helped the United States
expand its borders.

Lesson 1: Settling the South and Texas

Directions: Sequence the events in the order in which they took place by numbering them from 1 to 12. You may use your textbook.

____ Texas settlers decide to fight for their independence from Mexico, and in 1835 the Texas Revolution begins.

____ Spain sells Florida to the United States.

____ The Treaty of Guadalupe Hidalgo is signed, officially ending the war with Mexico.

____ Fearing a rebellion, Mexican leaders pass a law in 1830 forbidding new settlers from the United States.

____ Stephen F. Austin brings settlers to Texas, which is part of Mexico, under a land grant.

____ Mexico still thinks of Texas as part of Mexico and disagrees on the border between the United States and Mexico.

____ Texas leaders form the Republic of Texas on March 2, 1836.

____ Many Americans are against annexing Texas because it would expand slavery in the United States and could lead to war with Mexico.

____ Texas is annexed and becomes a state in 1845.

____ As an independent country, Texas faces problems such as defending itself and having no money. Many Texans want to be annexed to the United States.

____ Tensions grow between Mexico and the settlers from the United States because the settlers bring enslaved people with them to Texas.

____ Efforts to find a peaceful solution fail, and the Mexican War begins on May 13, 1846.

Notes for Home: Your child learned about the settlement of the South and how Texas became part of the United States.
Home Activity: With your child, review the sequence of events in Lesson 1, culminating in Texas becoming a state.

Name _____ Date _____

Lesson 2: Trails to the West

Directions: Write the number from each item in Column A on the line next to its example in Column B.

Column A	Column B
1. Period between 1840–1860 when more than 350,000 people moved to Oregon Country	_____ **a.** wagon train
	_____ **b.** Salt Lake City
2. First settlers to Oregon Country from the United States	_____ **c.** fur trappers and missionaries
3. Fur trappers in the West	_____ **d.** Oregon Trail
	_____ **e.** Brigham Young
4. Reason missionaries wanted to move to Oregon Country	_____ **f.** Oregon fever
5. The 2,000-mile route taken to Oregon Country by settlers	_____ **g.** The Mormon Trail
	_____ **h.** More settlers headed to Oregon Country
6. Treaty between the United States and Britain settling the border between Canada and Oregon caused this	_____ **i.** mountain men
7. A long line of covered wagons traveling to Oregon	_____ **j.** Mormons
	_____ **k.** teach Christian religion to Native Americans
8. Followers of the Church of Jesus Christ of Latter-day Saints	
9. Led the Mormons to found their own religious community	
10. Route taken by the Mormons from Illinois across the Great Plains and the Rockies	
11. Place founded by the Mormons in present-day Utah	

Notes for Home: Your child learned about people moving to the West along the Oregon and Mormon Trails.
Home Activity: With your child, discuss the difficulties families encounter as they move from one place to another.

Lesson 3: The Golden State

Directions: Fill in each missing cause or effect. You may use your textbook.

1. Cause

Gold was discovered at Sutter's Mill in California.

→

Effect

2. Cause

→

Effect

The number of people in San Francisco grew rapidly from 1848 to 1850.

3. Cause

→

Effect

Many people left California, but some stayed to become merchants who served miners.

4. Cause

Supplies and services were scarce but in high demand. Miners were willing to pay a lot of money for things.

→

Effect

5. Cause

→

Effect

Levi Strauss created sturdy pants out of canvas, and then denim, for the miners.

6. Cause

People moved from many places, including other countries, to get wealthy in the gold rush.

→

Effect

Notes for Home: Your child learned how the gold rush affected California and the people who rushed to move there.
Home Activity: With your child, discuss how your community began. Learn what businesses attracted settlers to your area and when the population expanded.

Name _____ Date _____

Evaluate Advertisements

An advertisement tries to sell people goods, services, or ideas. The purpose of all advertisement is to interest people in what the advertiser is trying to sell. Ads for women's apparel were common in the 1800s.

Directions: Read this sample advertisement, and answer the questions that follow.

WHITE SILK BONNETS ARE ELEGANT ADDITIONS TO A FINE LADY'S WARDROBE. YOU CANNOT OWN TOO MANY!

This lovely ladies' bonnet is made of cool silk, covered with white spotted tulle. The edges of the front are gently pleated, so as to give it a graceful and delicate appearance.

1. What is this advertisement selling?

_____

2. Who might be interested in this ad?

_____

3. What facts are stated about the product in the advertisement?

_____

_____

4. What words are used to encourage people to buy this item?

_____

_____

5. What, if anything, in the advertisement may be an exaggeration or inaccurate?

_____

_____

Notes for Home: Your child learned how to evaluate print advertisements.
Home Activity: Evaluate product advertisements in a magazine or on television. Identify the features of the product, then analyze the sales message for accuracy or exaggerated sales claims.

Vocabulary Review

Directions: Use the vocabulary words from Chapter 13 to complete each item. Use the numbered letters to answer the clue that follows.

1. Suffering unfair treatment __ __ __ __ __ __ __ __ __ __ __ __ __
                                                    1

2. People from all over the country rushed to California to find riches

   __ __ __ __ __ __ __ __
           9   11

3. A line of covered wagons traveling west __ __ __ __ __ __ __ __ __ __
                                                 2   12

4. Fur trapper in the West __ __ __ __ __ __ __ __ __ __ __
                                  3

5. Texas settlers' fight for independence from Mexico

   __ __ __ __ __ __ __ __ __ __ __ __ __ __
           7   13

6. Officially ended the Mexican War __ __ __ __ __ __ __ __ __

   __ __ __ __ __ __ __ __ __ __ __ __
                   4

7. Revolt by settlers leaves California independent from Mexico

   __ __ __ __ __ __ __ __ __ __ __ __
           5   8

8. To add a state to the Union __ __ __ __ __ __
                                            6

9. Someone who went to California during the gold rush

   __ __ __ __ __ - __ __ __ __ __
          15

10. Mexico and the United States at war over Texas

    __ __ __ __ __ __ __ __ __ __
       10   14

Clue: This policy expanded the nation from coast to coast.

__ __ __ __ __ __ __ __ __ __ __ __ __ __ __
1 2 3 4 5 6 7 8 9 10 11 12 13 14 15

Notes for Home: Your child learned how California and Texas became part of the United States.
Home Activity: With your child, locate Texas and California on a map of the United States. Use the scale to calculate how far settlers traveled from the East and Midwest to start a new life in these areas.

UNIT 6 Project   Lure of the Land

Directions: In a group, choose a trail that settlers might have taken. Then plan a travel program to share the settlers' experiences.

1. The trail our group chose is _____.

2. Some reasons settlers chose this trail:

   _____

   _____

   _____

   _____

3. The (✔) shows some of the details shown on our map:

___ trail we chose	___ mountains and other major landforms
___ other possible trails	___ dangers or points of interest on the trail
___ cities or towns	___ compass rose
___ state boundaries	___ scale
___ rivers and other bodies of water	___ key

4. Other materials we will use in our presentation:

   _____   _____   _____

✔ Checklist for Students

_____ We chose a settlers' westward trail.

_____ We researched reasons travelers used this trail to journey to the West.

_____ We identified some reasons the settlers chose this trail.

_____ We planned the features and details for our class.

_____ We identified props, costumes, sound effects, and other materials.

_____ We presented our travel program to the class.

Notes for Home: Your child learned about trails settlers used to journey to the West.
Home Activity: With your child, research how early settlers traveled to your community. From what areas did most of your first settlers come?

Name _____ Date _____

Main Idea and Details

Directions: Fill in the circle next to the correct answer.

Many people believe slavery in the United States ended with the Emancipation Proclamation. This idea is not completely accurate. The Emancipation Proclamation did outlaw slavery, but slavery continued in some areas.

Only certain people were declared free by the Emancipation Proclamation. Those people were slaves who lived in Confederate states that were fighting against the Union. Slaves who lived in border states that were fighting for the Union were not granted freedom by the

proclamation. Also unaffected were those slaves living in Southern areas already under Union control.

Although the Emancipation Proclamation granted legal freedom to slaves living in Confederate states that were fighting against the Union, those states did not recognize Lincoln's laws. Therefore, the slaves saw no change.

All slavery in the United States officially ended in December of 1865 with the passage of the Thirteenth Amendment to the Constitution.

1. How did the Emancipation Proclamation affect slavery?
   Ⓐ It freed all slaves in all states.
   Ⓑ It freed slaves in Union territory.
   Ⓒ It freed slaves in some states, but not in others.
   Ⓓ It did not free slaves.

2. Which slaves were not declared free by the Emancipation Proclamation?
   Ⓐ slaves who wanted to fight for the Union
   Ⓑ only African American women and children
   Ⓒ those in border states and areas under Union control
   Ⓓ only male slaves in border states

3. Why did slavery continue in Confederate states fighting against the Union?
   Ⓐ Those states did not recognize Lincoln's laws.
   Ⓑ The Union allowed it.
   Ⓒ The Thirteenth Amendment had not been passed.
   Ⓓ Those slaves did not want to move to the North.

4. What officially ended all slavery in the United States?
   Ⓐ the Emancipation Proclamation
   Ⓑ the passage of the Thirteenth Amendment to the Constitution
   Ⓒ the Civil War
   Ⓓ the Confederate states

 Notes for Home: Your child learned about identifying the main idea and details of a passage.
Home Activity: With your child, choose a magazine or newspaper article of interest and work together to identify the article's main idea and details.

Vocabulary Preview

Directions: Match each vocabulary word to its meaning. Write the vocabulary word on the line provided. Not all words will be used. You may use your glossary.

sectionalism	states' rights	secede
slave codes	Missouri Compromise	Confederacy
Underground Railroad	Fugitive Slave Law	Union
free state	Compromise of 1850	border state
slave state	Kansas-Nebraska Act	civil war

1. _____ to break away from

2. _____ state located between the Union and the Confederacy

3. _____ plan in which California entered the United States as a free state and the Fugitive Slave Law was passed

4. _____ states that remained loyal to the United States government

5. _____ state in which slavery was not allowed

6. _____ law which stated that escaped slaves had to be returned to their owners, even if they had reached Northern states where slavery was not allowed

7. _____ law allowing the people of Kansas and Nebraska to decide whether they would allow slavery in their territory

8. _____ organized, secret system set up to help enslaved people escape from the South to freedom in the North or Canada

9. _____ loyalty to a section or part of the country rather than to the whole country

10. _____ laws to control the behavior of slaves

11. _____ government formed by the seven seceding states, also known as the Confederate States of America

12. _____ state in which slavery was legally allowed

Notes for Home: Your child learned about problems between the North and the South and the compromises they developed.
Home Activity: Help your child learn the vocabulary terms by having him or her form comparisons between pairs of terms, such as *free state* and *slave state*, *Union* and *Confederacy*, and so on.

Lesson 1: North and South Grow Apart

Directions: Complete the compare-and-contrast table using information from Lesson 1. You may use your textbook.

Topic	In the North	In the South	Similar or Different?
The way of life in 1850			
Point of view on tariffs on imported goods			
Point of view on the buying and selling of manufactured goods			
Point of view on slavery			

Notes for Home: Your child learned about the different views of the North and the South during the mid-1800s.
Home Activity: With your child, discuss instances when your child's opinion or point of view might differ from that of a friend. Brainstorm positive ways to resolve or live with these differences.

Recognize Point of View

Point of view is the way a person looks at or thinks about a topic or situation and describes it. A person's point of view may be affected by his or her experiences and way of life.

Directions: Read the following poem. It was written by a Southern woman during the time when the South had to produce its own goods because it was blockaded by the North. Answer the questions that follow.

> My homespun dress is plain, I know;
>   My hat's palmetto, too.
> But then it shows what Southern girls
>   For Southern rights will do.
>   We send the bravest of our land
>   To battle with the foe,
> And we will lend a helping hand
>   We love the South, you know.
> Hurrah! Hurrah!
>   For the sunny South so dear.
> Three cheers for the homespun dress
>   That Southern ladies wear.

1. What is the topic of the poem?

    _____

2. What words does the writer use to show how she feels about Southern soldiers?

    _____

3. What words does the writer use to show how she feels about the South?

    _____

4. How do you think the writer feels about supporting the South in the war? How do you know?

    _____

    _____

    _____

    _____

    _____

Notes for Home: Your child learned to identify the writer's point of view.
Home Activity: With your child, discuss a family situation or a situation at school in which two people had different points of view. Help your child recognize that different points of view can come from different goals or experiences.

Lesson 2: Resisting Slavery

Directions: Categorize each term in the box by writing it in the column of the correct category below. You may use your textbook.

performed acts of cruelty	pretended to be sick
broke the tools they used	separated family members
learned to read	enforced slave codes
required permission to leave plantation	formed the Underground Railroad
used physical punishment	worked slowly

Methods of Controlling Slaves	Ways Slaves Resisted

Directions: Write the missing cause or effect on the line provided. You may use your textbook.

1. **Cause:** Slaves suffered cruel, harsh treatment.

   Effect: _____

2. **Cause:** _____

   Effect: Slave owners tried to prevent slaves from gathering and meeting with one another.

3. **Cause:** Captive Africans aboard the Spanish vessel *Amistad* seized the ship and ended up in the United States.

   Effect: _____

   _____

Notes for Home: Your child learned how slaves reacted to the treatment they received.
Home Activity: With your child, discuss how he or she feels when treated unfairly. Relate this feeling to how the slaves reacted when they were treated harshly and unfairly.

Name _____ Date _____

Lesson 3: The Struggle Over Slavery

Directions: Match each item in the first column to its clue or description in the second column. Write the number of the item on the line before its description.

1. Missouri Compromise

2. Fugitive Slave Law

3. Compromise of 1850

4. Kansas-Nebraska Act

5. *Uncle Tom's Cabin*

6. Dred Scott decision

7. John Brown's plan

8. Abraham Lincoln

9. Stephen Douglas

____ The Supreme Court ruled that slaves were not citizens of the United States and had no rights.

____ This book described the cruelties of slavery and won over many people to the abolitionist cause.

____ The people of each territory were allowed to decide whether it should be free or slave.

____ "If slavery is not wrong, then nothing is wrong. . . . [But I] would not do anything to bring about a war between the free and slave states."

____ Escaped slaves had to be returned to their owners, even if they had reached Northern states where slavery was not allowed.

____ A plan to attack pro-slavery people with weapons from the arsenal at Harper's Ferry further divided the North and the South in 1859.

____ The number of slave states and free states was kept balanced when Missouri was allowed into the Union as a slave state and Maine as a free state.

____ "Each state . . . has a right to do as it pleases on . . . slavery."

____ California became a free state, and the Fugitive Slave Law was passed.

Notes for Home: Your child learned about struggles over slavery that threatened to tear the United States apart.
Home Activity: With your child, choose a current controversial issue from the newspaper. Discuss citizens' opposing views and the divisions that can develop.

Name _____ Date _____

Lesson 4: The First Shots Are Fired

Directions: Sequence the events in the order in which they occurred by numbering them from 1 to 8. You may use your textbook.

_____ Lincoln asks Union states for troops to put down the Confederate rebellion.

_____ Abraham Lincoln is elected President of the United States.

_____ Some states are angered by Lincoln's call for troops. Virginia, Arkansas, Tennessee, and North Carolina secede and join the Confederacy.

_____ The Confederate States of America, or the Confederacy, is formed.

_____ The Confederates attack Fort Sumter, which is surrendered two days later. The Civil War has started.

_____ Jefferson Davis, president of the Confederacy, asks for the surrender of Union-held Fort Sumter in Charleston, South Carolina.

_____ The Southern states of South Carolina, Alabama, Florida, Mississippi, Georgia, Louisiana, and Texas secede.

_____ By Lincoln's inauguration on March 4, 1861, the Confederacy has control of most of the forts and military property in the South.

Directions: Explain each of the following points of view from the time of the American Civil War. You may use your textbook.

1. Explain the goal Lincoln and his supporters hoped to achieve by fighting the Civil War.

_____

_____

2. Explain the goal Southerners hoped to achieve by fighting the Civil War.

_____

_____

3. Why do you think Northerners called Southerners "rebels"?

_____

_____

_____

Notes for Home: Your child learned how different points of view in the United States led to the Civil War.
Home Activity: With your child, discuss how differing viewpoints often can be perceived as threats or hostility. Brainstorm ways that better communication and compromise can be used to prevent these types of misunderstandings.

Vocabulary Review

Directions: Choose the vocabulary word from the box that best completes each sentence. Write the word on the line provided. Not all words will be used.

sectionalism	states' rights	secede
slave codes	Missouri Compromise	Confederacy
Underground Railroad	Fugitive Slave Law	Union
free state	Compromise of 1850	border state
slave state	Kansas-Nebraska Act	civil war

1. The _____ was made up of states that remained loyal to the United States government.

2. The _____ allowed California to be admitted to the Union as a free state.

3. _____ is the idea that people of a state can choose the laws that best fit their needs.

4. South Carolina was the first state to _____ from the Union.

5. The _____ preserved the balance between free and slave states.

6. The states that seceded from the Union formed the _____.

7. The _____ allowed people in certain areas to determine whether or not their territory would allow slavery.

8. Although some former slaves had reached the North and found freedom, the _____ said they had to be returned to their owners.

9. _____ did not allow slaves to own land.

10. Slavery was illegal in California and any other _____.

11. Harriet Tubman became famous for helping slaves escape to freedom on the _____.

Notes for Home: Your child learned about differences between the North and the South that divided the nation.
Home Activity: Have your child practice using the vocabulary terms in sentences of his or her own.

Vocabulary Preview

Directions: Circle the vocabulary term that best completes each sentence.

1. The (Anaconda Plan, Reconstruction) was a three-part war strategy to crush the South during the Civil War.

2. Slavery was abolished by the (Thirteenth Amendment, Fourteenth Amendment) to the Constitution.

3. The (First Battle of Bull Run, Battle of Gettysburg) lasted three days and was one of the most important battles of the Civil War.

4. African Americans became U.S. citizens under the (Fourteenth Amendment, Thirteenth Amendment) to the Constitution.

5. At the (Battle of Antietam, Battle of Vicksburg), Union forces blockaded the city and bombarded it for 48 days.

6. (Segregation, Sharecropping) is the separation of blacks and whites.

7. Both the North and the South instituted the (blockade, draft) to get men to fight in the war.

8. The (Gettysburg Address, Emancipation Proclamation) granted freedom to slaves in any Confederate states that were still battling the Union.

9. The time after the war when the country was rebuilding and healing is known as (Reconstruction, segregation).

10. The (black codes, blockade) kept supplies from reaching Southern soldiers.

11. One of the early battles of the war was the (Battle of Gettysburg, First Battle of Bull Run).

12. People in many U.S. cities paid their respects to President Lincoln after his (assassination, impeachment).

13. The (Freedmen's Bureau, Emancipation Proclamation) was established to help former slaves after the war.

14. All male citizens received the right to vote with the ratification of the (Thirteenth Amendment, Fifteenth Amendment) to the Constitution.

15. The (Emancipation Proclamation, Jim Crow laws) enforced separation of blacks and whites.

16. Republicans in Congress called for the (total war, impeachment) of President Andrew Johnson.

Notes for Home: Your child learned about events during and after the Civil War.
Home Activity: With your child, review each vocabulary term and its definition to make sure the term fits in the sentence. Then make your own sentences using the vocabulary terms.

Lesson 1: The Early Stages of the War

Directions: Complete each compare-and-contrast table with information about the Union and the Confederacy. You may use your textbook.

	Supporters of the North	Supporters of the South
Reason for fighting		

	Northerners	Southerners
Believed advantage over the opposition		

	Union	Confederacy
War strategies		

Notes for Home: Your child learned about different attitudes toward war and different strategies used by the North and South during the Civil War.

Home Activity: With your child, discuss possible problems the Union and the Confederacy might have had to consider when forming their war strategies. Ask your child what could have gone wrong in each case.

Lesson 2: Life During the War

Directions: For each main idea, write a supporting detail on the line provided. You may use your textbook.

1. **Main Idea:** News of the war spread in many ways.

   Detail: _____

   _____

2. **Main Idea:** As the war continued, both sides had trouble getting more soldiers.

   Detail: _____

   _____

   _____

   _____

3. **Main Idea:** Most of the soldiers who died in the Civil War did not die in battle.

   Detail: _____

   _____

4. **Main Idea:** The Civil War did not begin as a war against slavery.

   Detail: _____

   _____

5. **Main Idea:** African Americans who wished to serve in the war were not treated the same as white soldiers.

   Detail: _____

   _____

   _____

   _____

6. **Main Idea:** Women contributed to the war effort in many ways.

   Detail: _____

   _____

   _____

   _____

 Notes for Home: Your child learned about difficult conditions during the war.
Home Activity: With your child, make a list of the difficulties soldiers and civilians experienced during the Civil War. Discuss how these types of difficulties might have made your family feel about the war, the enemy, and the country.

Lesson 3: How the North Won

Directions: Match each term in the box with its clue. Write the term on the line provided.

Battle of Gettysburg	Ulysses S. Grant	total war
Gettysburg Address	Battle of Vicksburg	Robert E. Lee
Anaconda Plan	William Tecumseh Sherman	Appomattox Court House

1. Place where Generals Lee and Grant met to discuss the terms of the Confederates' surrender of the Civil War _____

2. "I would rather die a thousand deaths." _____

3. President Lincoln made a short speech at a ceremony to dedicate a national cemetery. In his speech, Lincoln inspired the Union to keep fighting for a united nation and the end of slavery. _____

4. A method of warfare designed to destroy the opposing army and the people's will to fight _____

5. This three-day battle began on July 1, 1863. It was one of the most important battles of the Civil War. It was an important victory for the North and a costly battle for both sides. _____

6. Head of the Union forces in the Battle of Vicksburg _____

7. The surrender of this battle by the Southerners cut the Confederacy in two. _____

8. The Union blockade at the Battle of Vicksburg was part of this strategy to gain control of the Mississippi River and weaken the Confederacy. _____

9. Led soldiers in a destructive "March to the Sea" _____

Notes for Home: Your child learned how the North used strategies to win the Civil War.
Home Activity: With your child, brainstorm strategies for winning a game such as checkers, chess, or cards. Discuss the advantages of using a strategy to defeat an opponent.

Read a Road Map

A road map shows roads, cities, and places of interest. Drivers use road maps to figure out how to get from one place to another.

Directions: Use the road map to answer the following questions.

1. General Sherman's army probably walked and rode horses from Atlanta to Savannah, Georgia. What major roads might you take today to drive between these two cities?

   _____

2. What major city would you pass through when traveling along this route from Atlanta to

   Savannah? _____

3. According to this map, what other roads might you take to travel from Atlanta to

   Savannah? _____

4. Examine the map. Why do you think General Sherman's march was known as the "March

   to the Sea"? _____

   _____

5. General Sherman's army left Savannah and went to South Carolina. If you were to drive from Savannah to South Carolina today, what major road might you take?

   _____

Notes for Home: Your child learned how to read a road map.
Home Activity: With your child, look at a road map of your state. Together, determine the most direct route from your city to one of your state's borders. Next, find the most scenic route.

Name _____ Date _____

Use with Pages 516–521.

Lesson Review

Lesson 4: The End of Slavery

Directions: Define each term or phrase. Use a separate sheet of paper if you need more room. You may use your textbook.

1. Reconstruction _____

_____

2. Thirteenth Amendment _____

_____

3. black codes _____

_____

_____

_____

4. Freedmen's Bureau _____

_____

5. Ku Klux Klan _____

_____

6. Fourteenth Amendment _____

_____

7. Jim Crow laws _____

_____

8. sharecropping _____

_____

_____

Notes for Home: Your child learned about how the United States changed after the Civil War.
Home Activity: With your child, review the series of changes that took place during Reconstruction and discuss who benefited from each change.

Vocabulary Review

Directions: Use the vocabulary words from Chapter 15 to complete the following sentences. Write the correct word in the space provided. You may use your textbook.

1. _____ is the separation of blacks and whites.

2. The shutting off of an area by troops or ships to keep people and supplies from moving in or out is known as a _____.

3. At the Battle of _____, Union forces blockaded the city and bombarded it with cannon fire by land and sea for 48 days.

4. _____ is the practice of renting land from a landowner and paying rent with a portion of the crop produced on that land.

5. The murdering of a government or political leader is known as an _____.

6. Laws that denied blacks the right to vote or take part in jury trials were known as _____.

7. A method of warfare that destroys not only the opposing army but also the people's will to fight is known as _____.

8. In the Battle of _____, Union and Confederate forces clashed near the town of Sharpsburg in Maryland.

9. The First Battle of _____, one of the early battles of the Civil War, was won by the Confederates.

10. The _____ was established to help the more than 4 million former slaves after the war.

11. _____ refers to the rebuilding of the country after the Civil War.

12. The Battle of _____ lasted three days and was one of the most important battles of the Civil War.

13. _____ laws enforced the separation of blacks and whites.

14. The _____ Plan was a war strategy designed to "squeeze" the Confederacy.

Notes for Home: Your child learned about how the Civil War divided the nation and what steps were taken to heal and rebuild the country afterward.
Home Activity: With your child, analyze the relationships among the vocabulary terms for this unit. Begin by having your child place each term on a time line for the Civil War era.

Use with Page 528.

UNIT 7 Project History Speaks

Directions: In a group, prepare a talk that might have been given by a famous person who lived during the Civil War or Reconstruction.

1. We considered the following people who lived during the Civil War or Reconstruction as subjects for our talk:

   From the North   From the South

   _____   _____

   _____   _____

   _____   _____

2. Our group chose _____ from the candidates we considered.

3. Details from this person's life include:

   _____

   _____

   _____

   _____

   _____

4. _____ will play the part of _____ for our class presentation.

5. The (✔) shows visuals we presented to the class:

   ____ drawings ____ pictures ____ artifacts ____ other: _____

✔ Checklist for Students

_____ We identified a famous person to talk about the time period.

_____ We researched details about the life and times of this person.

_____ We named a group member to present the talk to the class.

_____ We showed visuals of Civil War life to the class.

Notes for Home: Your child helped prepare a first-person presentation on the Civil War period.
Home Activity: Ask your child to tell you about the historical figure his or her group selected. Encourage your child to share details about the life of this person.

Sequence

Directions: Fill in the circle next to the correct answer.

The United States began expanding westward during the 1800s. This expansion brought change to many people and parts of the nation.

As an increasing number of settlers moved west, the need for cross-country transportation and communication grew. Settlers on the frontier did not want to be isolated from friends and family back East.

Several new services were created to meet this need. First was the Pony Express. It lasted about a year until the first cross-country telegraph line was completed. A year later, in 1862, construction of the transcontinental railroad began.

At the same time the nation was laying railroad ties to link the East and West, the Homestead Act was encouraging people to settle the Midwest. The Homestead Act gave land to settlers. In 1877 many African American pioneers took advantage of the Homestead Act and settled Nicodemus, Kansas. Nicodemus became a bustling town and still lives on today as a symbol of freedom and opportunity.

In the Great Plains, Native Americans found their lives changing. In 1868 the U.S. government moved the Lakota people to the Great Lakota Reservation, an area that included the Black Hills. Just six years later, gold was found in the Black Hills, and the U.S. government again tried to move the Lakota. The Lakota refused to leave and defeated the United States in 1876 at the Battle of Little Bighorn, also known as Custer's Last Stand. One year later, the Lakota were defeated and moved to a new reservation.

1. Which of the following happened first?
   Ⓐ Lakota moved to the Great Lakota Reservation
   Ⓑ Nicodemus founded
   Ⓒ gold discovered in Black Hills
   Ⓓ Lakota defeated U.S. military

2. Which of the following shows the correct sequence of events?
   Ⓐ Nicodemus founded, Lakota Reservation created
   Ⓑ Battle of Little Bighorn, Pony Express established
   Ⓒ Lakota move to new lands, railroad construction begins
   Ⓓ Custer's Last Stand, African American pioneers found Nicodemus

Notes for Home: Your child learned how to sequence events that took place during the expansion of the United States.
Home Activity: Ask your child whether he or she would have liked to have lived during the time when the country was growing and technology was developing. Discuss why or why not.

Name _____ Date _____

Vocabulary Preview

Directions: Match each word with its meaning. Write the vocabulary word on the line next to its meaning. You may use your glossary.

Pony Express	Homestead Act	exoduster	reservation
telegraph	homesteader	cattle drive	Battle of Little Bighorn
transcontinental railroad	sodbuster	barbed wire	

1. _____ business in which mail was delivered by express riders on horseback

2. _____ twisted wire with sharp points used by homesteaders to keep cattle off their farmland

3. _____ government plan that offered free land to pioneers willing to start new farms on the Great Plains

4. _____ Lakota defeat of General George Custer's U.S. troops

5. _____ cowboys moving herds of cattle north to the railroad lines that extended across the Great Plains

6. _____ an African American pioneer who started a new life in Kansas or Nebraska

7. _____ a settler who claimed land through the Homestead Act

8. _____ an area of land set aside for Native Americans

9. _____ a Great Plains farmer who had to dig through the tough sod before planting crops

10. _____ replaced the Pony Express and sent messages along wires using electricity

11. _____ railroad that crossed the continent

Notes for Home: Your child learned about changes that occurred as the United States expanded.
Home Activity: Have your child practice the vocabulary words by using them in sentences of his or her own.

Lesson 1: Rails Across the Nation

Directions: Circle the answer that best completes each sentence.

1. In the 1850s thousands of miles of (railroad tracks, paved highways) crisscrossed the East.

2. The journey to the West by wagon or by ship could take (two weeks, months).

3. (Stagecoach, Pony Express) riders traveled in a horse-drawn wagon that traveled in stages, or short sections.

4. The (wagon train, Pony Express) delivered mail faster than was possible by stagecoach.

5. The (telegraph, stagecoach) put the Pony Express out of business.

6. Messages were sent along electrical wires in the form of (Navajo Code, Morse Code).

7. People were interested in building the (transcontinental railroad, stagecoach) to move people and goods across the nation.

8. Central Pacific workers began building tracks heading (east, west).

9. Both the Central Pacific and the Union Pacific had difficulties finding enough (workers, machines) for the huge project.

10. Union Pacific workers were challenged by (Native Americans, buffalo) when the tracks crossed hunting areas.

11. The railroad was completed when the tracks laid by Central Pacific and Union Pacific workers met at (Promontory Point, Salt Lake City) in Utah Territory.

Directions: Sequence the events below by drawing a line from each date in the first column to an event from that year in the second column.

1858	**a.** transcontinental railroad construction begins
1860	**b.** stagecoach travel begins
1861	**c.** transcontinental railroad is completed
1862	**d.** Pony Express delivery begins
1869	**e.** transcontinental telegraph communication begins

Notes for Home: Your child learned about early travel to the West and the building of the transcontinental railroad.
Home Activity: With your child, sequence the events involved in building the transcontinental railroad.

Name _____ Date _____

Time Zone Map

A time zone map tells you in what time zone a place is located. With this information you can figure out the time in other places across the country. Regardless of where you live, zones to the east of you are later than the zone in which you are located. Zones to the west of you are earlier.

Directions: Use the time zone map below to answer the questions that follow.

1. Suppose you were in Wichita, Kansas, and wanted to share some good news with your brother in Boston, Massachusetts. He gets home from work at 5:30 P.M. At what time might you place a call from your time zone to reach him at home after work?

   (A) 2:30 P.M.   (B) 2:45 P.M.   (C) 3:45 P.M.   (D) 4:45 P.M.

2. Bus, train, and airplane schedules list departure and arrival times according to the city in which each action takes place. Suppose you live in Dallas, Texas, and a relative is visiting from Los Angeles, California. The plane is scheduled to land in Dallas at 3:00 P.M. What time will it be in Los Angeles, when the plane lands in Dallas?

   (A) 12:00 P.M.   (B) 1:00 P.M.   (C) 4:00 P.M.   (D) 5:00 P.M.

3. Suppose you live in Las Vegas, Nevada, and you want to watch a live TV broadcast from Washington, D.C., scheduled to begin at 7:00 P.M. D.C. time. At what time should you tune in to the broadcast?

   (A) 4:00 P.M.   (B) 6:00 P.M.   (C) 9:00 P.M.   (D) 10:00 P.M.

4. Suppose you used an overnight delivery service to send a package from your home in Seattle, Washington, to a friend in Miami, Florida. The service promises to deliver the package by 10:00 A.M. Florida time. At what time can you call from Seattle to make sure your friend has received the package?

   (A) 1:00 A.M.   (B) 7:00 A.M.   (C) 12:00 P.M.   (D) 1:00 P.M.

 Notes for Home: Your child learned about time zones.
Home Activity: With your child, practice calculating time in other time zones. You may wish to use TV shows, travel schedules, or phone calls as examples.

Name _____ Date _____

Writing Prompt: Leaving Home

Long ago, the United States grew as Americans traveled westward. Many people left home for the first time to settle in a new place. Think about your first time away from home. How did you feel? What did you see? Write a paragraph to tell about it.

_____

_____

_____

_____

_____

_____

_____

_____

_____

_____

_____

_____

_____

_____

_____

_____

_____

_____

Notes for Home: Your child learned about transportation changes and westward expansion.
Home Activity: With your child, discuss some of the reasons people move. Compare and contrast reasons for moving today and long ago.

Lesson 2: Farmers and Cowboys

Use with Pages 546–552.

Directions: Answer the clues below. Then find and circle the answers in the puzzle.
Answers may appear horizontally, vertically, or diagonally in the puzzle.

```
T  B  V  J  X  H  O  M  E  S  T  E  A  D  E  R  S
G  R  A  S  S  H  O  P  P  E  R  S  L  X  C  T  G
O  T  A  W  K  Y  A  V  N  Z  C  O  W  T  O  W  N
D  Z  M  N  B  R  J  F  S  I  X  B  U  I  R  D  P
L  Q  E  X  S  O  D  B  U  S  T  E  R  S  Y  K  T
E  U  R  A  Y  C  M  X  Z  D  C  V  M  A  H  U  A
X  N  I  S  Z  L  O  N  G  H  O  R  N  S  O  R  F
O  E  C  B  G  W  E  N  A  Q  L  E  Z  P  M  W  Y
D  R  A  T  C  H  Y  S  T  Z  R  W  K  X  E  C  B
U  Y  F  Z  S  O  D  V  B  I  J  U  D  J  S  O  L
S  C  E  U  I  P  M  L  W  Y  N  Z  S  C  T  G  I
T  O  V  A  B  C  R  D  L  F  C  E  A  L  E  Y  Z
E  K  E  X  Q  J  E  Z  O  K  B  T  N  M  A  S  Z
R  A  R  N  J  B  W  G  Y  C  V  H  L  T  D  B  A
S  P  W  Y  R  X  S  L  A  Z  J  P  O  W  A  Z  R
F  M  C  A  T  T  L  E  D  R  I  V  E  X  C  L  D
H  V  B  Z  D  P  Y  K  M  O  W  H  E  A  T  Q  S
```

1. Offered free land to pioneer farmers
2. Settlers who claimed free land offered by the government
3. The ___ railroad helped bring settlers west.
4. Prairie grasses with thick, tangled roots
5. Farmers who had to dig through a layer of sod
6. In the winter, plains settlers faced deadly ___.
7. Millions of ___ ate the farmers' crops.

8. Europeans who wanted to move to the Great Plains had ___.
9. The Mennonites introduced a hardy type of ___.
10. Named themselves after the book of Exodus in the Bible
11. Tough breed of cattle: Texas ___
12. Began in Texas and ended in one of several towns along the railroad
13. Railroad town such as Abilene, Kansas
14. Twisted wire with sharp points

Notes for Home: Your child learned how the Great Plains became an important farming and ranching region.
Home Activity: Discuss with your child that people had to weigh the pros and cons of leaving their homes and moving west. Together, create a chart listing the pros and cons of moving to the Great Plains during the mid-1800s.

Lesson 3: War in the West

Directions: Sequence the events in the order in which they occurred. Number the events from 1 (earliest) to 10 (most recent). You may use your textbook.

_____ United States soldiers march into the Black Hills hoping to defeat the Lakota and move them onto a new reservation.

_____ Government leaders want to move Native Americans onto reservations to make room for expanding railroad lines and new farms, ranches, and mines.

_____ Railroads bring many settlers to the Great Plains. Farmers and ranchers begin fencing their land, and herds of buffalo begin to disappear.

_____ The United States and the Lakota sign a treaty creating the Great Lakota Reservation, which includes the Black Hills.

_____ The United States offers to buy land from the Lakota, but the Lakota refuse to sell.

_____ Native American writers and filmmakers continue to tell stories about their people's history and way of life.

_____ General Custer and his troops attack the Lakota, and all are killed in a battle known as the Battle of Little Bighorn.

_____ Native Americans see that their traditional way of life is being threatened.

_____ The Nez Percé surrender to the United States after being chased for 1,600 miles.

_____ Gold is found in the Black Hills, and miners illegally rush onto Lakota land.

Directions: Complete the cause-and-effect chart below.

Cause	Effect
Buffalo were hunted for their hides, for sport, and to feed railroad workers.	
	The Nez Percé fled and were pursued for three months by United States soldiers.

Notes for Home: Your child learned about struggles between Native Americans and the United States government as the West was settled.
Home Activity: With your child, discuss the causes and effects of the wars between the Native Americans and the U.S. government. Discuss what major changes were forced on Native Americans.

Name _____ Date _____

Vocabulary Review

Directions: Choose the vocabulary word below that best completes each sentence. Write the word on the line provided.

Pony Express	homesteader	barbed wire
telegraph	sodbuster	reservation
transcontinental railroad	exoduster	Battle of Little Bighorn
Homestead Act	cattle drive	

1. Two companies built the _____ to connect the country by rail.

2. An African American pioneer who started a new life in Kansas or Nebraska was an

   _____ .

3. _____ is used by farmers to create inexpensive fences to

   keep cattle off their farmland.

4. The government offered the _____, granting free land to

   pioneers willing to start new farms on the Great Plains.

5. Native Americans were moved to a _____, or land set aside

   by the government.

6. The _____ made mail delivery faster than by stagecoach.

7. U.S. General George Custer was killed in the _____.

8. A farmer on the Great Plains was known as a _____

   because of the tough soil in that area.

9. Cowboys participated in a _____ to get their cattle north to

   the railroad lines.

10. A _____ was someone who took advantage of the

    government plan to grant land to settlers who would farm the Great Plains.

11. With the invention of the _____, messages were sent along

    wires using electricity.

Notes for Home: Your child learned about changes that occurred as the nation expanded.
Home Activity: Practice the vocabulary words by having a spelling bee or a definition bee involving several friends or family members.

Vocabulary Preview

Directions: Write the definition of each term on the lines provided. You may use your glossary.

1. monopoly _____

_____

2. corporation _____

3. tenement _____

4. prejudice _____

5. settlement house _____

_____

6. labor union _____

_____

7. strike _____

_____

8. Spanish-American War _____

_____

_____

9. Rough Rider _____

_____

_____

10. Buffalo Soldier _____

_____

_____

 Notes for Home: Your child learned about life in the United States in the late 1800s.
Home Activity: Have your child write each vocabulary term in an original sentence. If he or she has difficulty, find the term in the text and explore how it is used.

Name _____ Date _____

Lesson 1: Inventions and Big Business

Directions: Match each person listed in the box below to an invention or accomplishment listed in the chart. Some answers will be used more than once. You may use your textbook.

John D. Rockefeller	Lewis Latimer	Andrew Carnegie
Alexander Graham Bell	Thomas Edison	Henry Bessemer

Invention/Accomplishment	Person Responsible
1. telephone	
2. phonograph	
3. helped make steel a major industry in the United States	
4. movie camera	
5. light bulb	
6. long-lasting light bulb	
7. gave away more than $300 million to help build universities, libraries, museums, and theaters	
8. founded Standard Oil	
9. new process for making steel	

Notes for Home: Your child learned about American entrepreneurs and inventors of the late 1800s.
Home Activity: With your child, brainstorm a list of benefits we enjoy today because of the accomplishments of the people listed in the chart.

Name _____ Date _____

Lesson 2: New Americans

Directions: Complete each sentence using terms and concepts from Lesson 2. Use an additional sheet of paper if you need more space. You may use your textbook.

1. During the late 1800s, many immigrants came to the United States from

   _____ .

2. During the early 1900s, many immigrants came to the United States from

   _____ .

3. Many Europeans left their homes to escape _____ such as hunger, poverty, lack of

   jobs, lack of freedom, and religious persecution.

4. For millions of European immigrants, _____ was their first stop in the United States.

5. Many Asian immigrants first came to _____ and waited there for permission

   to enter the United States.

6. Upon arriving in the United States, two things most immigrants did first were

   _____ and _____ .

7. Most immigrants settled in cities where there were busy _____ and many jobs.

8. Many immigrants and people from towns and farms moved into cities, causing a

   _____ .

9. _____ often provided unhealthy living conditions.

10. Although many immigrants faced _____, many received help in improving their lives.

11. Some people took jobs in crowded workshops known as _____, where

    conditions often were very dangerous.

12. To fight for better working conditions and better wages, many workers joined

    _____ .

13. Samuel Gompers founded the _____ to

    give unions more power.

Notes for Home: Your child learned about the lives of new immigrants to the United States during the late 1800s and early 1900s.
Home Activity: With your child, discuss the difficulties a new student at school might face and what your child might do to help that person with the adjustment. Compare this to the difficulties immigrants faced.

Lesson 3: Expansion Overseas

Directions: Complete the cause-and-effect chart with information from Lesson 3. You may use your textbook.

Cause	Effect
1. Russia offers to sell Alaska for 2 cents an acre. U.S. Secretary of State William Seward insists Alaska is worth buying.	
2.	Thousands of miners rush north in search of wealth and adventure.
3. American planters discover that the Hawaiian climate is good for growing sugarcane and pineapples.	
4. Queen Liliuokalani of Hawaii wants native-born Hawaiians to remain in control of the islands.	
5. Queen Liliuokalani yields her authority to the United States to avoid bloodshed.	
6.	Spanish soldiers imprison hundreds of thousands of Cubans to keep people from joining the revolution.
7. People in the United States are angered by Spain's treatment of the Cuban people. American-owned businesses in Cuba begin feeling the effects of the war.	
8.	Americans blame Spain for the explosion. Congress declares war on April 25, 1898, and the Spanish-American War begins.
9.	The United States emerges as a world power.

Notes for Home: Your child learned how the United States expanded and became a world power.
Home Activity: With your child, make a chart comparing and contrasting the ways the United States gained control of Alaska, Hawaii, Puerto Rico, the Philippines, and Guam.

Credibility of a Source

Some sources of information are more believable than others. This is due, in part, to who is presenting the information.

Directions: Read the two passages about General George Armstrong Custer and answer the questions that follow.

Passage A comes from a historical novel. The story is presented as a part-fact, part-fiction presentation of Custer's journal. As you read the words, imagine them to be directly from Custer, himself.

> *Perhaps I have worshiped my superiors too well with not enough thought of myself. [My wife,] Libbie, says that I have always been too hasty in putting the needs of others ahead of my own.*

Passage B comes from a biography. It is based on fact. At times the author includes a personal point of view or conclusion, as well as reports from others who were involved in the actual situation.

> *What [Custer] did was perfectly in keeping with his nature. He did what he had always done: push ahead, disregard orders, start a fight. . . .*

> *So he marched his men most of the night and flung them into battle when—as a number of Native Americans noted—they were so tired their legs shook when they dismounted.*

1. According to Passage A, how did Custer treat his superiors? According to Passage B?

   _____

   _____

2. According to Passage A, how did Custer treat others, in general? According to Passage B?

   _____

   _____

3. Which passage has more credibility? Why?

   _____

   _____

   _____

Notes for Home: Your child learned how to determine the credibility of a source.
Home Activity: With your child, brainstorm various sources of information and discuss the credibility of each.

Vocabulary Review

Directions: Read the following statements. Then write *T* (True) or *F* (False) on the
line before each statement. If the answer is false, correct the statement to make it
true. You may use your textbook. Not all words will be used.

_____ 1. A monopoly is any business that is owned by investors.

_____

_____ 2. In some cities, poor people received help at a settlement house.

_____

_____

_____ 3. The workers decided to stage a monopoly until the owners met their demands.

_____

_____

_____ 4. The African American soldiers who defended Americans and American property in
Cuba were known as Rough Riders.

_____

_____

_____ 5. A volunteer soldier under Theodore Roosevelt who defended Americans in Cuba was
known as a Rough Rider.

_____

_____

_____ 6. When a single company controls an entire industry and stops competition, it is called
a corporation.

_____

_____

_____ 7. A settlement house is a building that is divided into small apartments.

_____

_____

Notes for Home: Your child learned how industry and immigration affected the United States during the
mid-1800s to late 1800s.
Home Activity: With your child, take turns role-playing a situation for each vocabulary term. You may wish
to use real-life situations from the text as models.

Name _____ Date _____

UNIT
8 Project   Invention Conventions

Use with Page 592.

Directions: Make a poster or advertisement for an invention from the late 1800s.

1. The invention we chose is _____.

2. The name of the inventor is _____.

3. The purpose of the invention is _____.

4. Special features of this invention include _____.

5. The (✔) shows the benefits of this invention:

   ____ helping people   ____ saving money   ____ saving time   ____ other: _____

6. Reasons people should use this invention are _____.

7. This invention changed the world because _____

   _____.

8. This is what the invention looked like.

_____

_____

✔ **Checklist for Students**

____ We chose an invention from the late 1800s.

____ We identified the inventor, and we described the invention's purpose, features, and benefits.

____ We made a poster or advertisement for the invention.

____ We included a picture of the invention on the poster.

____ We presented our poster or advertisement to the class.

 Notes for Home: Your child researched an invention from the 1800s and advertised its features to the class.
Home Activity: With your child, identify a modern invention you both agree has changed the world. Discuss how it has impacted your life.

Summarize

Directions: Read the passage. Then fill in the circle next to the correct answer.

In the United States, civil rights are guaranteed to all citizens. However, this was not always true. African Americans and other minorities have long struggled for their civil rights in this country.

In 1892, the Supreme Court allowed segregation and "separate but equal" services for blacks and whites. Many African Americans felt that separate services, even in name, were unequal.

Change came about slowly. In 1950, during the Korean War, African American soldiers and white soldiers fought side by side. Four years later, the Supreme Court ruled that the segregation of public schools was illegal. One year later, an African American woman named Rosa Parks inspired the Montgomery bus boycott. In 1956, the Supreme Court ruled that segregation on public buses also was illegal.

Civil rights leaders such as Martin Luther King, Jr., and Malcolm X, and groups such as the NAACP emerged to support desegregation on all levels. Over time, this period became known as the Civil Rights Movement.

President John F. Kennedy added to the effort by proposing a new civil rights bill to better protect the rights of all citizens. The bill became law in 1964, after Kennedy's assassination.

The Civil Rights Act of 1964 banned segregation in all public places. The Voting Rights Act of 1965 protected all Americans' rights to vote. African Americans could no longer be prevented from voting. This finally gave them the power to change laws that they felt were unfair.

1. What was the direct result of the Montgomery bus boycott?
   Ⓐ Segregation in the military ceased to exist.
   Ⓑ Segregation on public buses was ruled illegal.
   Ⓒ Segregation of public schools ended.
   Ⓓ Segregation in all public places was ruled illegal.

2. How have civil rights changed in the United States since 1890?
   Ⓐ Separate but equal is considered fair for everybody.
   Ⓑ A civil rights bill now protects the rights of some citizens.
   Ⓒ Segregation is illegal and all citizens can vote.
   Ⓓ Segregation in the military is legal.

Notes for Home: Your child learned how to summarize a passage.
Home Activity: Ask your child to summarize a favorite story or event. Remind him or her that a summary has few details. Challenge your child to eliminate as many words as possible from his or her summary without making it ineffective.

Vocabulary Preview

Directions: Write the definition of each vocabulary term on the line provided. Use a separate sheet of paper if necessary. You may use your glossary.

1. Progressives _____

2. muckraker _____

3. isthmus _____

4. World War I _____

5. alliance _____

6. League of Nations _____

7. Treaty of Versailles _____

8. Nineteenth Amendment _____

9. Great Migration _____

10. assembly line _____

11. Harlem Renaissance _____

12. unemployment _____

13. stock market _____

14. Great Depression _____

15. New Deal _____

16. Dust Bowl _____

17. dictator _____

18. World War II _____

19. concentration camp _____

20. Holocaust _____

21. atomic bomb _____

Notes for Home: Your child learned about events in the early to mid-1900s.
Home Activity: Ask your child to use each vocabulary term in an original sentence.

Lesson 1: A Time of Reforms

Directions: Complete the chart by filling in the second column with the specific reform or reformer's main purpose or goal. You may use your textbook.

Reform/Reformer	Reform Goal
Theodore Roosevelt	
Progressives	
Muckrakers	
Sherman Antitrust Act	
Meat Inspection Act	
Pure Food and Drug Act	
Army doctors Walter Reed and W. C. Gorgas	

Notes for Home: Your child learned about reforms during Theodore Roosevelt's term of office.
Home Activity: With your child, read the label from any food package and discuss the importance of knowing which ingredients were used in preparing the food. Encourage your child to consider people's food allergies and other health issues.

Interpret Political Cartoons

A political cartoon is a drawing that shows people or
events in the news in a way that makes you smile or
laugh. The goal of political cartoons is to make
you think about events.

Directions: Use this cartoon about women's
rights to answer the questions below.

"MAKE WAY!"

1. Where do the women appear in
   this cartoon? What are they
   doing? Why do you think the
   cartoonist portrayed these
   characters as she did?

   _____

   _____

   _____

   _____

   _____

2. What do you think the signs in the cartoon represent?

   _____

3. In this cartoon, men are being pushed off the world. What do you think this means?

   _____

   _____

4. A woman named Laura Foster drew this political cartoon. How do you think she felt about
   women's rights? Explain.

   _____

   _____

   _____

Notes for Home: Your child learned how to interpret political cartoons.
Home Activity: With your child, look through recent newspapers or magazines to find a political cartoon.
Discuss the cartoon's message and the cartoonist's point of view.

Lesson 2: World War I

Directions: Read each cause below and write its effect on the line provided.

1. **Cause:** European nations compete with one another for land, trade, and military power.

   Effect: _____

2. **Cause:** In a telegram, Germany asks Mexico to enter the war on the side of the Central Powers. If Mexico agrees, Germany promises to help Mexico get back lands it had lost to the United States in the Mexican War. Soon after, Germany sinks American-owned trade ships.

   Effect: _____

3. **Cause:** As U.S. men enter World War I, U.S. women replace them in the workforce. Women argue that, since they can do the same jobs as men, they should be given the same right to vote.

   Effect: _____

4. **Cause:** The North promises better-paying jobs and less discrimination to Southern African Americans.

   Effect: _____

Directions: Circle the term that does not belong in each group. On the line, write why the term does not belong.

5. Britain, France, Russia, Switzerland

   _____

6. Australia, Austria-Hungary, Germany, Turkey

   _____

7. League of Nations, President Wilson, Red Cross, Treaty of Versailles

   _____

   _____

8. Nineteenth Amendment, Carrie Chapman Catt, Susan B. Anthony, W.E.B. DuBois

   _____

9. Ida Wells Barnett, W.E.B. DuBois, John Muir, Booker T. Washington

   _____

Notes for Home: Your child learned how World War I affected life in the United States.
Home Activity: With your child, make a list of jobs traditionally held by men and jobs traditionally held by women. Discuss how women's actions during World War I broke these traditional stereotypes. Ask your child how it might be unproductive to limit people to certain jobs simply because of their gender.

Name _____ Date _____

Use with Page 615.

Writing Prompt: New Inventions

The invention of the airplane had a major impact on the way in which World War I was fought. New inventions continue to be developed that change the way we live every day. What could you invent to change your life? Draw a picture of your invention. Write a paragraph to tell about it.

_____

_____

_____

_____

_____

_____

_____

_____

Notes for Home: Your child learned about the early planes used during World War I.
Home Activity: With your child, compare and contrast the technology used in World War I to the technology available to the military today. How might technological advances affect the ways in which a war is fought today?

Lesson 3: Times of Plenty, Times of Hardship

Directions: The chart contains important events in the postwar history of the United States. Complete the chart by matching each name or term from the box to one of the statements below. Not all words will be used.

Henry Ford	stock market crash	Charles Lindbergh	radio
Harlem Renaissance	severe drought	Eleanor Roosevelt	Amelia Earhart
Zora Neale Hurston	Social Security Act	Model T	Dust Bowl
bread lines	the Wright Brothers	Langston Hughes	high unemployment
Franklin D. Roosevelt	movies	CCC	cardboard shacks

Advances in Travel	The Roaring Twenties	The Great Depression	The New Deal
_____ _____ made the first successful powered airplane flight.	_____ moved from "silents" to "talkies," becoming a popular form of entertainment.	Farmers and factories produced more goods than consumers could buy, causing _____ _____.	_____ worked to help the jobless and the poor and rebuild the economy.
_____ was the first woman to fly solo across the Atlantic Ocean.	brought music, comedy, drama, sports, and news into people's homes.	As a result of the _____ _____, the economy went from boom to bust.	More than 2 million unemployed young men went to work for the _____.
_____ developed the assembly line and produced the _____.	A period of cultural growth that produced many famous African American artists was the _____ _____.	A _____ hit the Great Plains, earning the area the nickname the _____.	Passed in 1935, the _____ provided payments to the unemployed and the elderly.

Notes for Home: Your child learned about good times and difficult times in postwar America.
Home Activity: With your child, make a chart comparing life during the Roaring Twenties and the Great Depression. Discuss how today's economic situation is similar to and different from these two eras.

Name _____ Date _____

Lesson 4: World War II

Directions: Complete each summary chart below with information from Lesson 4. You may use your textbook.

Summary

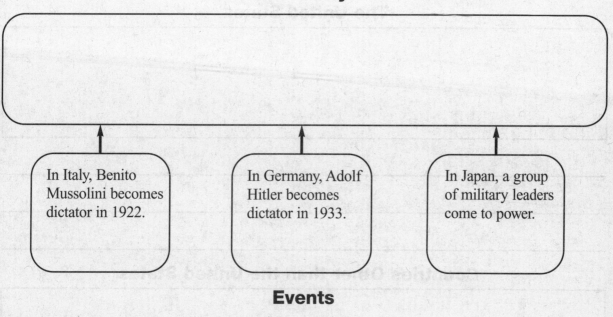

In Italy, Benito Mussolini becomes dictator in 1922.

In Germany, Adolf Hitler becomes dictator in 1933.

In Japan, a group of military leaders come to power.

Events

Summary

Important alliances are formed throughout Europe as dictators and military leaders begin trying to conquer and control more nations. The result is World War II.

Events

Notes for Home: Your child learned about World War II, its cause, and some of its effects.
Home Activity: With your child, discuss some of the reasons why countries declare war. Discuss whether war is ever justified and, if so, when. Examine with your child some of the far-reaching effects of war.

Vocabulary Review

Directions: Classify the vocabulary terms from Chapter 18 by listing each term in one of the categories below. On the lines below each box, write a sentence summarizing how the terms in that category are related.

The United States

_____

_____

Countries Other than the United States

_____

_____

Both the United States and Other Countries

_____

_____

Notes for Home: Your child learned about important events in the first half of the 1900s.
Home Activity: With your child, develop a one-minute oral summary of the first half of the twentieth century. Encourage your child to use as many of the vocabulary terms as possible in the summary.

Vocabulary Preview

Directions: Circle the term that best matches the definition or description.

1. Cold War   arms control

   A deal between the United States and the Soviet Union to limit the production of weapons

2. United Nations   civil rights

   An organization formed in 1945 consisting of 50 nations dedicated to finding peaceful solutions to international problems

3. Cold War   communism

   The long, bitter struggle between the United States and the Soviet Union

4. Internet   Iron Curtain

   A worldwide network of computers developed in the 1960s as a communication system that would continue working even after a nuclear attack

5. Vietnam War   Persian Gulf War

   War that began in 1990 when Iraq invaded its neighbor Kuwait, hoping to get Kuwait's rich oil supply

6. civil rights   legal rights

   The rights guaranteed to all citizens by the U.S. Constitution

7. communism   Iron Curtain

   A political and economic system in which the government owns all the businesses and land, and individuals have little personal freedom

8. space race   arms race

   The race between the United States and the Soviet Union to build more powerful weapons

9. Korean War   Persian Gulf War

   War that began in 1950 when communist North Korean forces invaded South Korea

10. Iron Curtain   Cuban Missile Crisis

    The line dividing the continent of Europe into communist and noncommunist countries

11. Cold War   Vietnam War

    War that began when communist North Vietnam attacked South Vietnam in an effort to unify all of Vietnam under communist rule

12. Watergate Scandal   Internet

    Scandal that forced President Richard Nixon to resign from office in 1974

Notes for Home: Your child learned about U.S. conflicts and compromises in the years after World War II.
Home Activity: With your child, write each vocabulary term on an index card and each definition on a separate card. Shuffle the cards and turn them all face down. Then have your child turn cards over one at a time to match each term with its definition. Be sure to turn the unmatched cards face down again.

Lesson 1: A Dangerous World

Directions: Complete each sentence with information from Lesson 1. Write the answer on the line provided. You may use your textbook.

1. The _____ is an organization formed in 1945 that promised that its 50 member nations would work to find peaceful solutions to international problems.

2. _____ and _____ were the world's two superpowers after World War II.

3. In 1945 the Soviet Union had a _____ government.

4. The United States and the Soviet Union had different views on communism, which resulted in the _____.

5. At the end of World War II, the nations in _____ were under Soviet control and established communist governments loyal to the Soviet Union.

6. The _____ divided the continent of Europe into communist and noncommunist countries.

7. The _____ was a program launched by U.S. President Harry S. Truman to help the nations of Western Europe recover from World War II.

8. The post-World War II military alliance formed by the United States and the nations of Western Europe was called the _____.

9. Through the Korean War, the United States was able to keep communism from spreading into _____.

10. In 1959, under leader Fidel Castro, Cuba became the first communist nation in the _____ Hemisphere.

11. In 1962 the United States took action to keep the Soviets from setting up nuclear missiles in Cuba. This was called the _____.

12. The _____, developed by the United States and the Soviet Union, is 1,000 times more powerful than the atomic bomb used in Hiroshima.

Notes for Home: Your child learned about the United States' determination to keep communism from spreading.
Home Activity: With your child, discuss why it might be important to keep communism from spreading in other parts of the world. Ask your child what causes he or she thinks might justify getting involved in a war.

Lesson 2: Struggle for Equal Rights

Directions: Match each term in the box to its description. Write the answer on the line provided.

Harry S. Truman	Rosa Parks	Sandra Day O'Connor
separate but equal	Martin Luther King, Jr.	NOW
Thurgood Marshall	Civil Rights Act of 1964	Shirley Chisholm
civil rights	Malcolm X	Dolores Huerta

1. _____ The rights that are guaranteed to all citizens by the Constitution

2. _____ Tried to convince the Supreme Court to declare that segregation is illegal under the Constitution

3. _____ Was the inspiration for the Montgomery bus boycott

4. _____ Civil rights leader who urged African Americans to rely on themselves to bring change

5. _____ Ordered an end to segregation in the military in 1948

6. _____ Supreme Court language that allowed segregated public services and schools for African Americans

7. _____ Women's rights organization formed in 1966 to fight for fair pay and equal opportunities for women

8. _____ First African American woman elected to Congress

9. _____ Helped create a union to improve the lives of migrant farm workers

10. _____ Law banning segregation in all public places in the United States

11. _____ In 1981 became the first woman named to the Supreme Court

12. _____ Organized a march in Washington, D.C., in August 1963, calling for an end to prejudice

---

Notes for Home: Your child learned about women's and African Americans' struggles for equal rights.
Home Activity: Discuss with your child how he or she likes to be treated when playing with other children. Ask him or her to explain the idea of fairness and then work together to brainstorm examples of fair and unfair treatment.

Lesson 3: The Cold War Continues

Directions: Write the letter of the effect on the line beside each cause. You may use your textbook.

Cause	Effect

Cause

____ 1. Soviets launch Sputnik.

____ 2. Soviets send the first man to orbit Earth.

____ 3. Vietnam gains independence from France.

____ 4. North Vietnam tries to unite all of Vietnam under communist rule.

____ 5. U.S. armed forces go to Vietnam.

____ 6. In April 1975, South Vietnam surrenders to North Vietnam.

____ 7. U.S. President Nixon tries to change the Cold War relationship between the United States and China.

____ 8. Nixon and Soviet leaders sign an arms control agreement.

____ 9. Nixon is involved in the Watergate scandal.

____ 10. U.S. President Jimmy Carter tries to bring peace to Israel and Egypt.

____ 11. Cold War tensions increase when Soviet troops invade Afghanistan in December 1979.

Effect

a. Vietnam is united under communist rule.

b. U.S. leaders fear that the Soviets will use their new knowledge about space exploration to attack the United States.

c. Each side agrees to limit nuclear weapons, and tensions are eased.

d. South Vietnam resists communism and the Vietnam War begins.

e. President Jimmy Carter objects to the Soviets' attempt to expand their power and refuses to send U.S. athletes to the 1980 Olympics in Moscow.

f. Nixon becomes the only President to resign from office.

g. In an effort to win the space race, the U.S. works toward being the first country to send a person to the moon.

h. Americans are divided on the issue of U.S. involvement in the Vietnam War.

i. Nixon is successful in trying to improve relations and, in 1972, becomes the first U.S. President to visit China.

j. Leaders of Israel and Egypt visit the United States and sign a peace treaty in March 1979.

k. Vietnam is split into North Vietnam and South Vietnam.

Notes for Home: Your child learned about Cold War tensions between the United States and the Soviet Union.
Home Activity: With your child, discuss the positive and negative effects of the Cold War on the United States and the world. Ask your child how the space race and the arms race might have had different results if the United States and the Soviet Union had worked together rather than against each other.

Name _____ Date _____

Understand Map Projections

A map projection is a way to show the round Earth on a flat surface. Because Earth is a sphere, all map projections have errors in size, shape, distance, or direction.

Directions: Use the maps on this page to answer the questions below. Use a separate sheet of paper if you need more space.

Map A

Projection: _____

Map B

Projection: _____

1. Of the two maps shown here, which is the Mercator projection? Which is an equal-area projection? Label the maps accordingly. _____

   _____

2. What types of distortion are found on a Mercator projection? _____

   _____

   _____

3. Compare the continent of South America on the two map projections above. What

   difference, if any, do you see? _____

   _____

   _____

4. Which map projection should you use to accurately compare the sizes of Greenland and

   South America? Why? _____

   _____

Notes for Home: Your child learned about map projections and their distortions.
Home Activity: Using the maps on this page or in the textbook, work with your child to compare the distances between lines of latitude on each map. Explain that uneven distances are a clue to one type of map distortion.

Name _____ Date _____

Lesson 4: Looking Toward the Future

Directions: Sequence the events in the order in which they occurred. Number them from 1 (earliest) to 10 (most recent). You may use your textbook.

____ The Berlin Wall is destroyed, and several communist governments in Eastern Europe are replaced with elected governments.

____ Newly elected U.S. President Ronald Reagan believes the United States should strengthen its military to block Soviet efforts to expand communism around the world.

____ The United States leads a group of more than 20 nations in Operation Desert Storm, an attack on Iraqi forces in Kuwait.

____ The 2000 U.S. presidential election is one of the closest races in history. George W. Bush wins the electoral college vote, and Al Gore wins the popular vote. George W. Bush is declared President.

____ The Soviet Union and the United States sign an arms control agreement in which both countries agree to destroy some of their nuclear weapons.

____ The Soviet Union breaks up into 15 independent republics, and Gorbachev announces that the Cold War is over.

____ During his second term in office, President Clinton faces a scandal and is impeached.

____ The Middle Eastern nation of Iraq invades Kuwait in an effort to take control of Kuwait's rich oil supply. This begins the Persian Gulf War. The United States must decide whether to help end the conflict.

____ Soviet leader Mikhail Gorbachev begins reforming the country by allowing people more political and economic freedom.

____ U.S. President William Clinton appoints Madeleine Albright as secretary of state. She is the first woman to hold this position.

Directions: In recent decades, many changes have occurred in politics, science, technology, and culture. What is one change that you think will occur in the next 50 years? Why?

_____

_____

_____

Notes for Home: Your child learned about changes in politics and technology that will affect the future.
Home Activity: With your child, discuss inventions and other changes that might take place during this century. Ask whether your child thinks each potential change will have positive or negative effects on the world and why.

Vocabulary Review

Directions: Use the vocabulary words from Chapter 19 to complete the crossword puzzle.

Across

4. Iraq invaded Kuwait, sparking the _____ _____ War.

7. Fifty nations dedicated to finding peaceful solutions to international problems

9. A political and economic system in which the government owns all the businesses and land

12. The line dividing the continent of Europe into communist and noncommunist countries

13. The war that started when North Vietnam tried to unify all of Vietnam under communist rule

14. Worldwide network of computers

Down

1. The _____ War started when the North Koreans invaded South Korea.

2. The long, bitter struggle between the United States and the Soviet Union was called the _____ War.

3. The contest to be first to explore outer space was known as the _____ race.

5. The _____ _____ Crisis happened when the Soviets sent nuclear weapons to Cuba.

6. The U.S. Constitution guarantees these to all citizens.

8. The U.S. and Soviet Union's competition to build more weapons was known as the _____ race.

10. Because of an arms _____ agreement, the United States and the Soviet Union limited the number of weapons they produced.

11. President Nixon resigned for his involvement in the _____ scandal.

Notes for Home: Your child learned about events in the second half of the 1900s.
Home Activity: With your child, play a game of "Name That War," in which you supply details and your child supplies the name of the specific war from this chapter.

Name _____ Date _____

UNIT
9 Project   Then and Now

Use with Page 674.

Directions: In a group, plan a documentary about historic events and advances in technology during a decade from the 1900s.

1. We chose the decade 19____–19____.

2. The (✔) shows which topics we researched:

   ____ historic events   ____ technological advances   ____ transportation   ____ entertainment

   ____ clothing   ____ home life   ____ education   ____ occupations

   ____ other: _____

3. The following people from the decade will speak for the documentary:

   Name: _____   Role: _____

   Name: _____   Role: _____

   Name: _____   Role: _____

4. My role in the documentary is _____.

5. Questions about living in the 19____s:

   _____

   _____

   _____

6. Answers to questions about the 19____s:

   _____

   _____

   _____

✔ Checklist for Students

_____ The group chose a decade from the 1900s.

_____ The group researched topics about living in the 19__s.

_____ Roles were assigned for the documentary.

_____ The group wrote questions and answers about the decade.

_____ The group presented its documentary to the class.

Notes for Home: Your child participated in a group presentation on a decade from the 1900s.
Home Activity: Discuss with your child your favorite decade of the twentieth century. Describe the clothing, home life, transportation, and important events of this time period.

Main Idea and Details

Learning to find the main idea and details will help you understand most kinds of writing. The most important idea about a topic is its main idea. The ideas that give more information about the main idea are its supporting details.

Directions: Read the paragraph. Then read each question. Fill in the circle next to the correct answer.

> One reason the United States is so diverse is that immigrants have come here from all over the world. About 1,000 years ago, Europeans began traveling to North America as explorers. Five hundred years ago Spain, sent explorers such as Christopher Columbus and Juan Ponce de León. The French were soon to follow. French explorers Jacques Cartier and Samuel de Champlain landed in what is now Canada. The English then sent explorers John Cabot and Henry Hudson, among others. They hoped to catch up with the French and Spanish in the race to establish colonies in North America. Many people also arrived from Africa. Today people from around 200 different countries live in the United States.

1. What is the main idea of the paragraph?
   - (A) Portugal was the first to send out explorers.
   - (B) About 500 years ago, Europeans began traveling to explore the Americas.
   - ● One reason the United States is so diverse is that immigrants have come here from all over the world.
   - (D) People from around 200 different countries live in the U.S. today.

2. Which explorer helped the English try to catch up to its rival explorers?
   - (A) Christopher Columbus
   - ● John Cabot
   - (C) Hernando de Soto
   - (D) Samuel de Champlain

3. Which country sent Columbus and Ponce de León?
   - (A) France
   - (B) England
   - (C) Portugal
   - ● Spain

Notes for Home: Your child learned to identify the main idea and details of an assigned reading selection.
Home Activity: With your child, skim a brief newspaper article. Ask your child to identify the main idea and details of the story.

Vocabulary Preview

Directions: Match each vocabulary word to its meaning. Write the vocabulary word on the line after the definition. You may use your glossary. Not all words will be used.

culture
ideal
ethnic group
census
immigrant
democracy
republic
constitution
citizen
private property
economy
free enterprise
profit
supply
demand
export
import

1. a good that one country buys from another **import**
2. a good that one country sells to another **export**
3. written plan of government **constitution**
4. all the things that surround us, including air, water, land, trees **environment**
5. amount of a product that is available **supply**
6. business of growing crops and raising animals **agriculture**
7. government's count of the people in a country **census**
8. fuel formed from the remains of plants and animals that lived thousands of years ago **fossil fuel**
9. government in which the people elect representatives to make laws and run the government **republic**
10. important belief **ideal**
11. large area with common features that set it apart from other areas **region**
12. member of a country **citizen**
13. method of bringing water to dry land **irrigation**
14. moisture that falls to Earth in the form of rain, sleet, or snow **precipitation**
15. money a business has left over after it has paid all its costs **profit**

---

consumer
entrepreneur
region
geography
agriculture
irrigation
climate
precipitation
interdependent
natural resource
mineral
fossil fuel
renewable resource
nonrenewable resource
conservation
environment
pollution

16. economy in which people start their own businesses and own their own property **free enterprise**
17. person who leaves one country to go live in another **immigrant**
18. people who share customs and language **ethnic group**
19. person who buys or uses goods and services **consumer**
20. person who starts a new business, hoping to make a profit **entrepreneur**
21. preserving and protecting resources **conservation**
22. resource that can be replaced **renewable resource**
23. resource that cannot easily be replaced **nonrenewable resource**
24. the way of life of a group of people **culture**
25. something owned by an individual **private property**
26. substance found on Earth that is neither animal nor vegetable **mineral**
27. system for producing goods and services **economy**
28. addition of harmful substances to the air, water, or soil **pollution**
29. weather in an area over a long period of time **climate**
30. the study of Earth and how people use it **geography**

Notes for Home: Your child learned several terms that are helpful when studying the United States.
Home Activity: Write definitions and terms on separate index cards. Play a matching game to build comprehension of each word.

Lesson 1: The American People

Directions: Answer the following questions on the lines provided. You may use your textbook.

1. What is the meaning of the motto, or short saying, on the Great Seal?
   Out of many people, states, and backgrounds, one country was formed.

2. The motto on our nation's Great Seal was representative of the United States when it first became a country. Why do you think the motto still represents our country today?
   Possible answer: Today people still come from many different countries all around the world to become a part of this one country.

3. What are the two largest ethnic groups in the United States today?
   Whites, Hispanics

4. What are two reasons early immigrants left their homelands and came to the land known today as the United States?
   Possible answers: To find land of their own, to have the freedom to live and worship as they saw fit, or that they were enslaved.

5. What do you think the words "indivisible, with liberty and justice for all," found at the end of the Pledge of Allegiance, mean?
   Possible answer: The country will not be divided; it will stand united, as one nation; and it will provide freedom and justice for all its people.

Notes for Home: Your child learned that the people of the United States share many ideals.
Home Activity: Discuss the importance of symbols to this country. With your child, review citizens' responsibilities in upholding the Pledge of Allegiance.

Chart and Graph Skills
Use with Pages 12–13.

Read Line and Circle Graphs

Graphs show information in a visual way. A line graph shows change over time. A circle graph shows a whole divided into parts. These graphs use rounded numbers.

Directions: Read each graph and answer the questions that follow.

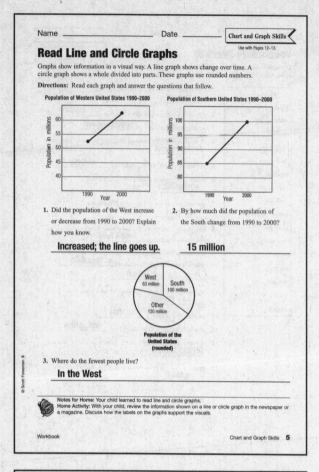

Population of Western United States 1990–2000

Population of Southern United States 1990–2000

1. Did the population of the West increase or decrease from 1990 to 2000? Explain how you know.

   Increased; the line goes up.

2. By how much did the population of the South change from 1990 to 2000?

   15 million

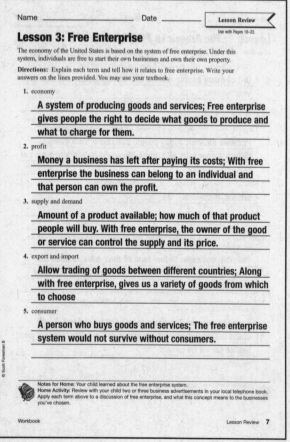

West 63 million
South 100 million
Other 120 million

Population of the United States (rounded)

3. Where do the fewest people live?

   In the West

Notes for Home: Your child learned to read line and circle graphs.
Home Activity: With your child, review the information shown on a line or circle graph in the newspaper or a magazine. Discuss how the labels on the graphs support the visuals.

© Scott Foresman 5

Lesson Review
Use with Pages 14–17.

Lesson 2: Government by the People

Directions: Draw a line from each item in column A to its example in column B.

Column A

1. republic
2. Abraham Lincoln
3. John F. Kennedy
4. United States Constitution
5. elected representatives

Column B

a. our government is "of the people, by the people, and for the people"

b. "We the people of the United States . . ."

c. ". . . ask not what your country can do for you—ask what you can do for your country."

d. the people elect representatives to make laws and run the government

e. President of the United States and members of Congress

Directions: Complete the flow chart using the terms in the box.

freedom of religion	obey the law	right to vote
freedom of speech	respect the rights of others	rights
involvement in government	responsibilities	

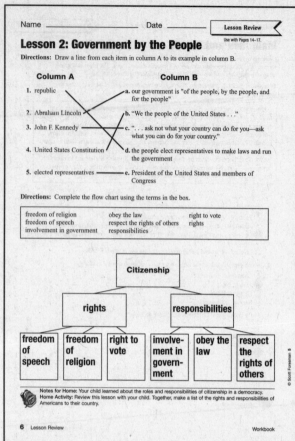

Citizenship

rights — responsibilities

freedom of speech | freedom of religion | right to vote | involvement in government | obey the law | respect the rights of others

Notes for Home: Your child learned about the roles and responsibilities of citizenship in a democracy.
Home Activity: Review this lesson with your child. Together, make a list of the rights and responsibilities of Americans to their country.

© Scott Foresman 5

Lesson Review
Use with Pages 18–22.

Lesson 3: Free Enterprise

The economy of the United States is based on the system of free enterprise. Under this system, individuals are free to start their own businesses and own their own property.

Directions: Explain each term and tell how it relates to free enterprise. Write your answers on the lines provided. You may use your textbook.

1. economy

   A system of producing goods and services; Free enterprise gives people the right to decide what goods to produce and what to charge for them.

2. profit

   Money a business has left after paying its costs; With free enterprise the business can belong to an individual and that person can own the profit.

3. supply and demand

   Amount of a product available; how much of that product people will buy. With free enterprise, the owner of the good or service can control the supply and its price.

4. export and import

   Allow trading of goods between different countries; Along with free enterprise, gives us a variety of goods from which to choose

5. consumer

   A person who buys goods and services; The free enterprise system would not survive without consumers.

Notes for Home: Your child learned about the free enterprise system.
Home Activity: Review with your child two or three business advertisements in your local telephone book. Apply each term above to a discussion of free enterprise, and what this concept means to the businesses you've chosen.

© Scott Foresman 5

Lesson Review
Use with Pages 24–30.

Lesson 4: Land and Regions

Directions: Write the name of the region described on the lines provided. Some regions are described more than once.

| Northeast | Southeast | Midwest | Southwest | West |

1. This region is divided into two smaller regions—New England and the Middle Atlantic states.

   Northeast

2. The Grand Canyon is in this region.

   Southwest

3. The nation's largest city, New York City, is located in this region.

   Northeast

4. Some of the country's highest mountains are in this region.

   West

5. Two of the nation's largest port cities, Baton Rouge and New Orleans, Louisiana, are located in this region.

   Southeast

6. Big Bend National Park is located in this region.

   Southwest

7. This region produces more corn than any other region in the country.

   Midwest

8. This region of the United States is the largest in area.

   West

Notes for Home: Your child learned the five regions of the United States.
Home Activity: With your child, review the map on pp. 26–27. Discuss the geography and the climate of the region in which you live.

© Scott Foresman 5

Map and Globe Skills

Use with Pages 32–33.

Read an Elevation Map

An elevation map shows the elevation, or height, of land. Elevation is measured above or below sea level. The map shows the elevation for the states of Massachusetts and Rhode Island.

Directions: Read the map and answer the questions that follow.

1. At what elevation range are most of the large cities on this map found? **0–700 feet**

2. What is the elevation of Boston, Massachusetts? **0–700 feet**

3. Starting at Mt. Greylock, how many feet would a person have to descend to reach sea level? **About 3,487 feet**

4. Which labeled river in Massachusetts is at the highest elevation? **Deerfield River**

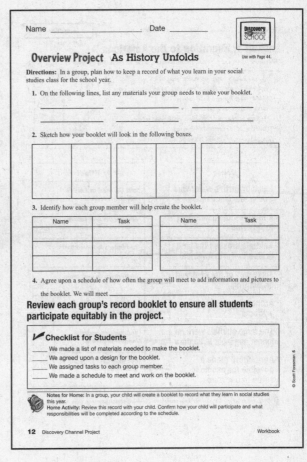

Notes for Home: Your child learned to read an elevation map.
Home Activity: With your child, use an elevation map to identify areas in the United States with the highest or lowest elevations. Discuss the concept of sea level, at 0 feet of elevation.

Lesson Review

Use with Pages 34–38.

Lesson 5: Resources and the Environment

Directions: Complete the chart with information from this lesson.

Important Resources	Why They Are Important	Two Examples
natural resources	to provide food and shelter	soil, trees, water, fish
minerals	for building materials	copper, granite, aluminum, gold, salt
fossil fuels	used for energy	oil, coal, natural gas
renewable resources	many uses; can be replaced	trees, water, fish, deer
nonrenewable resources	many uses; cannot be replaced easily	fossil fuels, including coal, oil, natural gas
national parks	to protect the environment	Yellowstone, Mount McKinley, Everglades

Notes for Home: Your child learned about America's reliance on its natural resources.
Home Activity: Walk around your home with your child. Identify the renewable and nonrenewable resources your family consumes regularly.

Vocabulary Review

Use with Overview Unit.

Vocabulary Review

Directions: Choose the vocabulary word from the box that best completes each sentence. Write the word on the line provided. Not all words will be used.

culture	private property	entrepreneur	mineral
ideal	economy	region	fossil fuel
ethnic group	free enterprise	geography	renewable resource
census	profit	agriculture	nonrenewable resource
immigrant	supply	irrigation	conservation
democracy	demand	climate	environment
republic	export	precipitation	pollution
constitution	import	interdependent	
citizen	consumer	natural resource	

1. A **census** tells how many people live in a country.

2. Someone who moves to another country is an **immigrant**

3. A written plan of government is known as a **constitution**.

4. A **citizen** is a member of a country.

5. Our economy is based on a system of **free enterprise**

6. Entrepreneurs start businesses to earn a **profit**

7. Import and **export** is buying and selling goods between countries.

8. Each person who buys or uses a good is a **consumer**.

9. **Irrigation** can help farmers grow crops in dry areas.

10. **Climate** is the weather of a certain place over a period of time.

Notes for Home: Your child learned several terms related to the republic of the United States.
Home Activity: Have your child restate key concepts of this chapter to you, using the above terms in the descriptions.

Discovery SCHOOL

Overview Project   As History Unfolds

Use with Page 44.

Directions: In a group, plan how to keep a record of what you learn in your social studies class for the school year.

1. On the following lines, list any materials your group needs to make your booklet.

   _____   _____   _____
   _____   _____   _____

2. Sketch how your booklet will look in the following boxes.

3. Identify how each group member will help create the booklet.

Name	Task		Name	Task

4. Agree upon a schedule of how often the group will meet to add information and pictures to the booklet. We will meet _____

Review each group's record booklet to ensure all students participate equitably in the project.

✔ **Checklist for Students**
_____ We made a list of materials needed to make the booklet.
_____ We agreed upon a design for the booklet.
_____ We assigned tasks to each group member.
_____ We made a schedule to meet and work on the booklet.

Notes for Home: In a group, your child will create a booklet to record what they learn in social studies this year.
Home Activity: Review this record with your child. Confirm how your child will participate and what responsibilities will be completed according to the schedule.

Summarize

A summary tells the main ideas of a paragraph, section, or story. A good summary is short and tells the most important ideas. It should not include many words or details.

Directions: Read the paragraph. Then answer the questions that follow. Fill in the circle next to the correct answer.

> Many scholars believe that people first migrated to the Americas in different ways. Some believe that the Bering Strait became shallower, exposing the land below the water and forming a land bridge between Asia and the Americas. Others believe that people arrived by boat. Despite questions as to how they arrived, people believe that the first Americans moved from North America to South America. They adapted to their new environments by changing their way of living to meet the challenges of each environment.

1. Which sentence is the BEST summary of the paragraph?
   - ● Many scholars believe that people migrated to the Americas, moving from north to south, and adapting their culture to meet their environment.
   - Ⓑ Some people believe that the Bering Strait became shallower, exposing a land bridge between Asia and the Americas.
   - Ⓒ People moved to new environments, adapting their lifestyle to their environment.
   - Ⓓ Some people believe the first people to migrate to America arrived by boat.

2. In which part of the paragraph do you look to find the summary?
   - Ⓐ detail
   - Ⓑ body text
   - Ⓒ last sentence
   - ● topic sentence

3. Which is important to include in a summary?
   - Ⓐ all names, dates, and facts
   - Ⓑ supporting details
   - Ⓒ name of the source or author
   - ● main ideas

Notes for Home: Your child learned to summarize a paragraph, section, or story.
Home Activity: Have your child summarize the day's activities, giving the most important ideas with few words or details.

Workbook   Reading Social Studies 13

Vocabulary Preview

Directions: Match each vocabulary word to its meaning. Write the vocabulary word on the line after the definition. You may use your glossary.

Ice Age	artifact	drought	pyramid
glacier	archaeologist	civilization	empire
migrate	ceremony	surplus	tribute
theory	mesa	specialize	slavery

1. a long period without rain __drought__
2. thick sheets of ice __glacier__
3. movement of people to another land __migrate__
4. a possible explanation __theory__
5. an object that someone made in the past __artifact__
6. do only one kind of job __specialize__
7. activity done for a special purpose or event __ceremony__
8. high, flat landform that rises steeply from the land around it __mesa__
9. culture with organized system of government, religion, and learning __civilization__
10. long period of extreme cold on Earth __Ice Age__
11. a group of lands and peoples ruled by one leader __empire__
12. the practice of holding people against their will __slavery__
13. more than is needed __surplus__
14. payment demanded by rulers from the people they rule __tribute__
15. one who studies artifacts of people __archaeologist__
16. building shaped like a triangle __pyramid__

Notes for Home: Your child learned terms about early life in the Western Hemisphere.
Home Activity: Help your child learn these terms by making flashcards (with a term on one side and the definition on the other) to review each word.

14 Vocabulary Preview   Workbook

Lesson 1: Migration to the Americas

Directions: Complete the cause-and-effect chart, using the phrases in the box.

- Much of Earth's water was frozen into glaciers
- Agriculture made it possible for people to settle in one place
- A land bridge linked Asia to America
- Archaeologists study artifacts
- The large animals were no longer available to hunters
- Their way of life centered on hunting
- Animals crossed the land bridge to North America

Cause	Effect
Much of Earth's water was frozen into glaciers	and the level of Earth's oceans dropped.
A land bridge linked Asia to America	and people and animals migrated to the Americas.
Animals crossed the land bridge to North America	so hunters followed them.
Their way of life centered on hunting	so hunters moved often.
Archaeologists study artifacts	and draw conclusions about people from long ago.
The large animals were no longer available to hunters	and hunters became hunter-gatherers.
Agriculture made it possible for people to settle in one place	because people began to grow their food.

Notes for Home: Your child learned how people migrated to the Americas.
Home Activity: Have your child share examples of cause-and-effect relationships in his or her daily life.

Workbook   Lesson Review 15

Read Climographs

Directions: Read the climograph and answer the questions that follow.

	Temperature		Precipitation	
	°F	°C	in.	cm.
January	30	-1	3	8.2
February	32	0	3	6.9
March	41	5	4	11.2
April	52	11	4	10.2
May	61	16	4	11.0
June	70	21	4	9.9
July	74	23	4	11.0
August	72	22	4	10.2
September	66	19	3	8.0
October	54	12	3	6.9
November	42	6	3	8.2
December	32	0	3	7.8

1. What two kinds of information are shown in a climograph?
   __Average temperature and precipitation__
2. Which two months shown have the same average temperature?
   __February, December__
3. What is the warmest month on the climograph?
   __July__
4. Which month has the lowest average temperature?
   __January__
5. Which month has the highest average precipitation?
   __March__
6. Which months are the driest?
   __February, October__

Notes for Home: Your child learned to read a climograph.
Home Activity: Draw a climograph like the one shown. With your child, plot the daily high and low temperatures and precipitation in your area for a week.

16 Chart and Graph Skills   Workbook

Lesson 2: Early American Cultures

Directions: Match each clue to its culture. Write the name of the culture on the line. Some cultures will be used more than once. You may use your textbook.

Mound Builders   Anasazi   Inuit

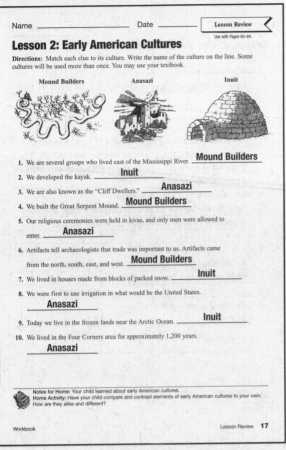

1. We are several groups who lived east of the Mississippi River. **Mound Builders**

2. We developed the kayak. **Inuit**

3. We are also known as the "Cliff Dwellers." **Anasazi**

4. We built the Great Serpent Mound. **Mound Builders**

5. Our religious ceremonies were held in kivas, and only men were allowed to enter. **Anasazi**

6. Artifacts tell archaeologists that trade was important to us. Artifacts came from the north, south, east, and west. **Mound Builders**

7. We lived in houses made from blocks of packed snow. **Inuit**

8. We were first to use irrigation in what would be the United States. **Anasazi**

9. Today we live in the frozen lands near the Arctic Ocean. **Inuit**

10. We lived in the Four Corners area for approximately 1,200 years. **Anasazi**

Notes for Home: Your child learned about early American cultures.
Home Activity: Have your child compare and contrast elements of early American cultures to your own. How are they alike and different?

Lesson 3: The Rise of Empires

Directions: Complete the Venn diagram by writing the terms and phrases in the box in the correct section of the diagram. You may use your textbook.

roads linked to capital city	Atlantic to Pacific empire	present-day Peru
fastest communication system	worshipped many gods	floating gardens
one of the world's largest cities	system of writing	terraces
worshipped god of war	pyramids	farmers
people specialized	calendar	conquerors
produced food surplus		

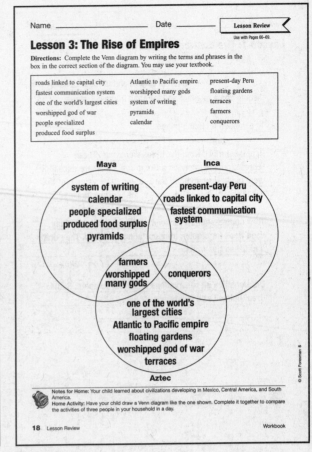

Maya — **system of writing, calendar, people specialized, produced food surplus, pyramids**

Inca — **present-day Peru, roads linked to capital city, fastest communication system**

Maya/Aztec — **farmers, worshipped many gods**

Inca/Aztec — **conquerors**

Aztec — **one of the world's largest cities, Atlantic to Pacific empire, floating gardens, worshipped god of war, terraces**

Notes for Home: Your child learned about civilizations developing in Mexico, Central America, and South America.
Home Activity: Have your child draw a Venn diagram like the one shown. Complete it together to compare the activities of three people in your household in a day.

Vocabulary Review

Directions: Choose the vocabulary word from the box that best completes each sentence. Write the word on the line provided. Not all words will be used.

Ice Age	artifact	drought	pyramid
glacier	archaeologist	civilization	empire
migrate	ceremony	surplus	tribute
theory	mesa	specialize	slavery

1. The ruler demanded that his people pay him **tribute**

2. An **archaeologist** is a person who studies people from long ago.

3. A thick sheet of ice is known as a **glacier**

4. The ruler's vast **empire** contained many peoples and lands.

5. A stone arrowhead made long ago is an **artifact**

6. The lack of rain caused a **drought** and problems for farmers.

7. The Maya **civilization** developed an extremely accurate calendar.

8. The Anasazi people **specialize** in basket weaving.

9. The **Ice Age** was an extremely cold period of time on Earth.

10. A building shaped like a triangle with the point at the top is called a **pyramid**

11. Animals and people move, or **migrate**, to new lands.

12. **Slavery** is when people are held against their will and do not have their freedom.

13. The unneeded **surplus** food was traded for needed things.

14. The landform known as a **mesa** means table in Spanish.

Notes for Home: Your child learned terms about early life in the Western Hemisphere.
Home Activity: Have your child use these vocabulary words to tell you a story about early civilizations.

Vocabulary Preview

Directions: Match the underlined vocabulary word to its meaning. Write the letter for the meaning of each underlined word on the line. You may use your glossary.

1. Members of a tribe share a common culture. **B**

2. People on the hunt lived in tepees. **F**

3. Wampum belts and necklaces are special. **E**

4. The shaman will cure your illness. **I**

5. The Iroquois lived in the Eastern Woodlands cultural region. **M**

6. The people formed a league to support peace. **C**

7. The totem pole showed a person's wealth. **N**

8. The Pueblo Indians developed a village way of life. **J**

9. A Plains Indian lived in a lodge. **A**

10. The hosts of the potlatch gave gifts. **L**

11. You can see traditional dances at a powwow. **K**

12. They used a travois to carry the buffalo. **G**

13. Many Native Americans live on a reservation. **H**

14. A longhouse is an Iroquois building used for shelter. **D**

a. Round hut built over a deep hole
b. Group of families with one leader
c. Organization for a specific purpose
d. Very long Iroquois building
e. Polished seashells on strings or woven into belts
f. Shelter made of a circle of poles and buffalo hides
g. Poles to which a load was tied for transport
h. Land set aside by the U.S. government
i. Healer
j. Spanish word for village
k. American Indian gathering to keep traditions alive
l. Type of party; word meaning "to give away"
m. Area in which people with similar cultures live
n. A carved post with animals or other images

Notes for Home: Your child learned about terms related to Native Americans.
Home Activity: With your child, select one Native American group and find out about its culture.

Lesson 1: The Eastern Woodlands

Directions: Answer the following questions on the lines provided.

1. What did members of the Seneca, Cayuga, Onondaga, Oneida, Mohawk, and Tuscarora tribes share? **A common culture and purpose caused them to come together and form the Iroquois League.**

2. What was the purpose of the Iroquois League?
To establish a lasting peace

3. What were the different roles of men and women in the Iroquois League?
Representatives from the tribes were men. These representatives attended a Great Council where decisions were made that affected the League. Older women of the tribes chose, and could remove, the representatives.

4. How did the Iroquois use the natural resources of the Woodlands? Name at least three ways.
They hunted animals for food, clothing, and tools. They used trees for shelter, transportation, and food. They drank and fished the water.

5. What is one way the Iroquois today have changed? What is one way they are the same as in their past?
Different: live on reservations, build skyscrapers; Same: Great Council still meets

Notes for Home: Your child learned about the American Indians of the Eastern Woodlands and the Iroquois League.
Home Activity: Have your child compare ways Native Americans gave thanks to practices in your culture.

Lesson 2: The Great Plains

Directions: Answer the following questions on the lines provided.

1. What effect did dry land have on the Plains Indians?
They settled along rivers so they could have water for their crops.

2. How were the Plains Indians' lives affected by the buffalo?
The buffalo provided a major source of meat. The hides were made into articles such as clothes and blankets. The horns were made into bowls, and the stomach was used as a cooking pot for stew.

3. What methods did the Plains Indians use to hunt buffalo?
They ran the buffalo off of cliffs or wore animal disguises to get near enough to use their bows and arrows.

4. How did the Cheyenne use horses?
To raid other tribes, as an item of value to trade, to transport hunters and goods, and to pull the travois

5. In which present-day state do many of the Cheyenne live?
Montana

Notes for Home: Your child learned about the tribes of the Great Plains.
Home Activity: Have your child explain how the horse changed the lives of the American Indians.

Internet Research

Directions: Answer the following questions on the lines provided.

1. Why is it important to use only reliable reference sources when doing research on the Internet?
Accept all reasonable answers. A reliable source will give you good information.

2. When searching on the Internet, what is the effect of putting a phrase in quotes?
It tells the computer that the topic you want is a complete phrase.

3. What is one disadvantage of doing research on the Internet?
Possible answers: It may be difficult to narrow the search sufficiently to find the needed information; not all information is reliable.

4. What is one advantage of doing research on the Internet?
The information may be more current than from a printed book.

Directions: Complete the flowchart using the sentences in the box.

Pick Web sites to visit.	Choose a topic. Choose a search engine.
Type in the keywords.	Narrow the search, if necessary.

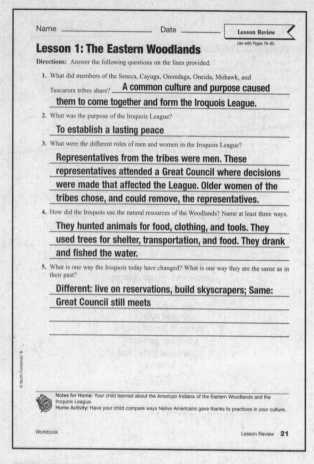

1. Choose a topic.
2. Choose a search engine.
3. Type in the keywords.
4. Narrow the search, if necessary.
5. Pick web sites to visit.

Notes for Home: Your child learned about doing research on the Internet.
Home Activity: Work with your child on your home or local library computer to research a topic of your child's choice.

Lesson 3: The Southwest Desert

Directions: Match each term in the box to its description. Write the term on the line. Some terms will be used more than once.

Apache	Navajo	Pueblo Indians	kachina	snake dance	Oraibi

1. Ceremony that dancers hope will bring rain
snake dance

2. Lived a village way of life based on farming
Pueblo Indians

3. Thought to be descendents of the Anasazi
Pueblo Indians

4. A tribe of hunters
Apache

5. Hopi and Zuni tribes
Pueblo Indians

6. A tribe who raised sheep
Navajo

7. Dolls used to educate young Hopi about their religion
kachina

8. Hopi village built on a mesa
Oraibi

Notes for Home: Your child learned about the tribes of the Southwest.
Home Activity: Help your child draw a picture or use modeling clay to make a Pueblo village.

Lesson 4: The Northwest Coast

Directions: Explain each term. Tell how each item was used by the people of the Northwest Coast. Write your answers on the lines provided. You may use your textbook.

1. potlatch

   A party at which the guests receive gifts from the hosts. A potlatch is a way of gaining respect in the community.

2. hunting and gathering

   This was the way the people got their food.

3. totem pole

   A carved post with animals or other images representing a person's ancestors; Totem poles were a way to gain respect and show wealth.

4. dugout canoe

   Master carvers would carve a canoe out of a single cedar log. Dugout canoes were used to hunt at sea.

5. blankets and copper shields

   Common gifts given at a potlatch

6. shaman

   A person people went to when they were not feeling well; Becoming a shaman was a way to gain respect.

7. masks, rattles, and serving dishes carved from wood

   The objects reflected a respect for the spirits around the people.

Notes for Home: Your child learned about tribes of the Northwest Coast.
Home Activity: Review the above items with your child. Together, rank each item from 1 to 7 to indicate how important each item was to the people of the Northwest Coast.

© Scott Foresman 5

Vocabulary Review

Directions: Choose the vocabulary word from the box that best completes each sentence. Write the word on the line provided.

tribe	wampum	travois	totem pole
league	reservation	powwow	shaman
cultural region	lodge	pueblo	
longhouse	tepee	potlatch	

1. The son carved a ___totem pole___ to show his ancestry and wealth.
2. The goods and belongings were carried on a ___travois___.
3. The ___shaman___ used special items to cure people.
4. All the members of the ___tribe___ listened to the chief.
5. While out on a hunt, the women put up the ___tepee___.
6. A ___longhouse___ can be as long as half a football field.
7. A ___lodge___ is a building in which the Plains Indians lived.
8. They will host a ___potlatch___ with gifts for everyone.
9. They formed a ___league___ to make peace.
10. Some Native Americans today still live on a ___reservation___.
11. You may be able to buy ___wampum___ at the ___powwow___.
12. ___Pueblo___ is the Spanish word for *village* and the name of a group of people who lived in the Southwest Desert ___cultural region___

Notes for Home: Your child learned about terms related to Native Americans.
Home Activity: Quiz your child on proper spelling and usage of these vocabulary words.

© Scott Foresman 5

Vocabulary Preview

Directions: Read each sentence. Match the underlined word in each sentence with its synonym or definition below. Write the word on the line. You may use your glossary.

The emperor ruled the people fairly.
The sailors used a magnetic compass to find their way home.
The people in the caravan brought gold and other goods to the city.
The people went on a pilgrimage to the holy land.
The astrolabe helped map makers.
The saga has been told for thousands of years.
A great deal of growth took place during the Renaissance.
Sailors use navigation to guide their ships.
Many people were captured and sold in the slave trade.

1. ___saga___ Long spoken tale repeated from one generation to the next
2. ___magnetic compass___ Tool used by sailors to determine their direction at sea
3. ___navigation___ Science sailors use to plot their course and find their location far from land
4. ___caravan___ Group of traders traveling together
5. ___slave trade___ Buying and selling of human beings
6. ___pilgrimage___ Journey taken for religious reasons
7. ___emperor___ Ruler of an empire
8. ___astrolabe___ Tool that used the sun and stars to find a location based on its distance from the equator
9. ___Renaissance___ Period of time that marked a new beginning in arts and sciences and a desire to learn more about the world

Notes for Home: Your child learned terms about early life in the Eastern Hemisphere.
Home Activity: With your child, read a newspaper article about scientific exploration. Discuss the tools scientists used to make their discoveries.

© Scott Foresman 5

Lesson 1: Traveling Asia's Silk Road

Directions: Match each term to one explorer. Write the term on a line on the graphic organizer.

Africa	gunpowder	India	silk cloth
China, 1405	paper money	Red Sea	Silk Road
coal	magnetic compass	sailor	Venice, 1271
East Indies	Persian Empire	merchant	tea and spices

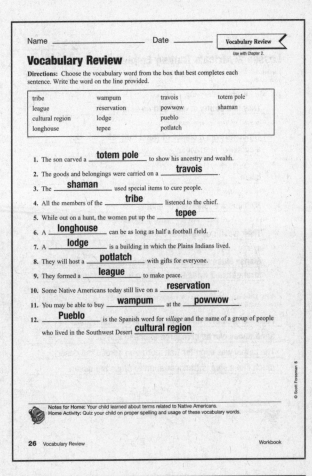

Notes for Home: Your child learned about the journeys of Marco Polo and Zheng He.
Home Activity: Visit the local library or search the Internet with your child to find out more about one of the places mentioned in this lesson.

© Scott Foresman 5

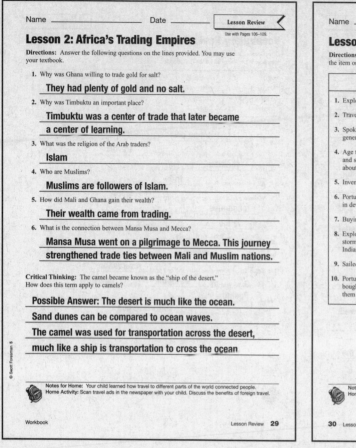

Lesson 2: Africa's Trading Empires

Use with Pages 106–109.

Lesson Review

Directions: Answer the following questions on the lines provided. You may use your textbook.

1. Why was Ghana willing to trade gold for salt?

   They had plenty of gold and no salt.

2. Why was Timbuktu an important place?

   Timbuktu was a center of trade that later became a center of learning.

3. What was the religion of the Arab traders?

   Islam

4. Who are Muslims?

   Muslims are followers of Islam.

5. How did Mali and Ghana gain their wealth?

   Their wealth came from trading.

6. What is the connection between Mansa Musa and Mecca?

   Mansa Musa went on a pilgrimage to Mecca. This journey strengthened trade ties between Mali and Muslim nations.

Critical Thinking: The camel became known as the "ship of the desert." How does this term apply to camels?

Possible Answer: The desert is much like the ocean. Sand dunes can be compared to ocean waves. The camel was used for transportation across the desert, much like a ship is transportation to cross the ocean

Notes for Home: Your child learned how travel to different parts of the world connected people.
Home Activity: Scan travel ads in the newspaper with your child. Discuss the benefits of foreign travel.

© Scott Foresman 5

Lesson 3: European Explorers

Use with Pages 110–115.

Lesson Review

Directions: Match each item in Column A with its example in Column B. Write the number of the item on the line.

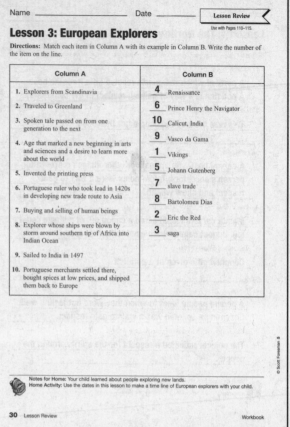

Column A	Column B
1. Explorers from Scandinavia	**4** Renaissance
2. Traveled to Greenland	**6** Prince Henry the Navigator
3. Spoken tale passed on from one generation to the next	**10** Calicut, India
4. Age that marked a new beginning in arts and sciences and a desire to learn more about the world	**9** Vasco da Gama
5. Invented the printing press	**1** Vikings
6. Portuguese ruler who took lead in 1420s in developing new trade route to Asia	**5** Johann Gutenberg
7. Buying and selling of human beings	**7** slave trade
8. Explorer whose ships were blown by storm around southern tip of Africa into Indian Ocean	**8** Bartolomeu Dias
9. Sailed to India in 1497	**2** Eric the Red
10. Portuguese merchants settled there, bought spices at low prices, and shipped them back to Europe	**3** saga

Notes for Home: Your child learned about people exploring new lands.
Home Activity: Use the dates in this lesson to make a time line of European explorers with your child.

© Scott Foresman 5

Use Parallel Time Lines

Use with Pages 116–117.

Chart and Graph Skills

Directions: The parallel time lines you used on pp. 116–117 are horizontal. Parallel time lines can also be vertical. Look at the vertical time lines on this page. Notice the dates and the continent each time line represents. Now look at the events in the box. Write each event in sequence on the correct country time line.

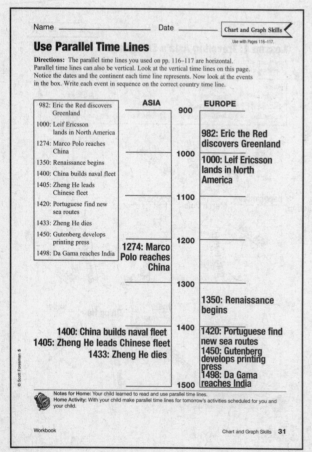

	ASIA		EUROPE
982: Eric the Red discovers Greenland		900	
1000: Leif Ericson lands in North America			**982: Eric the Red discovers Greenland**
1274: Marco Polo reaches China		1000	**1000: Leif Ericsson lands in North America**
1350: Renaissance begins			
1400: China builds naval fleet		1100	
1405: Zheng He leads Chinese fleet			
1420: Portuguese find new sea routes		1200	**1274: Marco Polo reaches China**
1433: Zheng He dies			
1450: Gutenberg develops printing press		1300	
1498: Da Gama reaches India			**1350: Renaissance begins**
	1400: China builds naval fleet	1400	**1420: Portuguese find new sea routes**
	1405: Zheng He leads Chinese fleet		**1450: Gutenberg develops printing press**
	1433: Zheng He dies		**1498: Da Gama reaches India**
		1500	

Notes for Home: Your child learned to read and use parallel time lines.
Home Activity: With your child make parallel time lines for tomorrow's activities scheduled for you and your child.

© Scott Foresman 5

Vocabulary Review

Use with Chapter 3.

Vocabulary Review

Directions: Choose the vocabulary word from the box that best completes each sentence. Write the word on the line provided.

emperor	pilgrimage	Renaissance
magnetic compass	astrolabe	navigation
caravan	saga	slave trade

1. The **caravan** crossed the desert on camelback.

2. My brother went on a **pilgrimage** to Mecca last year.

3. The **saga** of the journey to the new land was passed down from one generation to the next.

4. The **astrolabe** is a tool that uses stars to determine distance from the equator.

5. A **magnetic compass** will help you locate north, south, east, and west.

6. **Navigation** is a science sailors use to guide them on the ocean.

7. Many cultural advances took place during the **Renaissance**

8. The **emperor** ruled a vast empire.

9. **Slave trade**, or the business of buying and selling human beings, has existed for many centuries.

Directions: Write an original paragraph in the space below. Use as many of the vocabulary words as you can.

_____

_____

_____

_____

Notes for Home: Your child learned terms about early life in the Eastern Hemisphere.
Home Activity: Encourage your child to use each vocabulary word in an original sentence.

© Scott Foresman 5

Top-left panel

Name _____ Date _____

Discovery SCHOOL

1 Project Early Cultures Documentary

Use with Page 124.

Directions: Plan a documentary about an early eastern or western culture. In a group, create a storyboard that describes the culture. Present the storyboard to the whole class.

- The culture for our documentary is _____
- The title of our documentary is _____
- The (✔) shows the topics covered in our storyboard:

___ peak period   ___ rulers   ___ significant dates and events

___ trade   ___ population   ___ accomplishments

___ important monuments   ___ important artifacts   ___ other interesting facts

- Our storyboard plan is below. Each storyboard describes a different picture.

1	2	3	4
5	6	7	8

If students need additional space, have them copy the storyboard onto larger sheets of paper. Instruct students to write their paragraphs next to, or under, each frame of the storyboard.

✔ **Checklist for Students**

___ We chose an early culture.
___ We gave the documentary a title.
___ We sketched our storyboard about the culture.
___ On a separate page, we wrote a paragraph describing each picture.
___ Our group presented the storyboard for our documentary to the class.

Notes for Home: Your child learned about early cultures.
Home Activity: With your child, research the cultural background of your family. Using online references or primary sources, find out more about your cultural heritage.

Workbook   Discovery Channel Project   **33**

© Scott Foresman 5

Top-right panel

Name _____ Date _____

Reading Social Studies
Use with Pages 130–131.

Sequence

The sequence of events is the order in which things happen. Finding the sequence of events is especially helpful when you are reading about history. Dates and words such as *first, then, after, once, afterwards,* and *later* help signal the sequence of events.

Directions: Read the paragraph, and then read each question. Fill in the circle next to the correct answer.

> First, Spain sent ships across the Atlantic. Spanish explorer Christopher Columbus sailed in 1492. After Columbus's first voyage, Spain sent more explorers. The Spanish conquered the Aztecs in 1521. Almost 100 years after Columbus's first voyage, English colonists attempted to set up a colony on Roanoke Island in 1587. Later, in 1624, the Dutch started New Amsterdam.

1. Which of the following countries was the first to send explorers to the Americas?
   - ● Spain
   - Ⓑ France
   - Ⓒ Holland
   - Ⓓ England

2. In which year were the Aztecs conquered?
   - Ⓐ 1624
   - Ⓑ 1492
   - ● 1521
   - Ⓓ 1587

3. Who started New Amsterdam?
   - Ⓐ the English
   - Ⓑ the Spanish
   - Ⓒ the French
   - ● the Dutch

Notes for Home: Your child has been learning to find the sequence of events in a passage.
Home Activity: Have your child use word and date clues to tell you about recent events and activities in his or her life.

34   Reading Social Studies   Workbook

© Scott Foresman 5

Bottom-left panel

Name _____ Date _____

Vocabulary Preview
Use with Chapter 4.

Vocabulary Preview

Directions: Read each vocabulary word from Chapter 4 in the box below. Then write each word in its definition on the lines provided. You may use your textbook.

expedition	conquistador	convert	plantation	missionary
colony	ally	colonist	encomienda	mission
Columbian Exchange	conquest	society		

1. A **society** is a group of people forming a community.

2. A **mission** is a religious settlement where a **missionary** group lives and works.

3. To **convert** means to change.

4. A **conquest** is the capture or taking of something by force.

5. An **expedition** is a journey made for a special purpose.

6. An **ally** is a friend who will help in a fight.

7. A **conquistador** is a Spanish conqueror.

8. A **colony** is a settlement far from the country that rules it.

9. A **colonist** is a person who lives in a colony.

10. The **Columbian Exchange** is a movement of people, animals, plants, diseases, and ways of life between the Eastern Hemisphere and Western Hemisphere.

11. An **encomienda** is a large piece of land, usually given to its owners by the king of Spain.

12. A **plantation** is a large farm with workers who live on the land they work.

Notes for Home: Your child learned about Spain's colonization of the Americas.
Home Activity: Practice saying, spelling, and using these vocabulary words correctly with your child.

Workbook   Vocabulary Preview   **35**

© Scott Foresman 5

Bottom-right panel

Name _____ Date _____

Lesson Review
Use with Pages 134–138.

Lesson 1: The Voyages of Columbus

Directions: Answer the questions below on the lines provided. You may use your textbook.

1. What was one possible reason the Europeans wanted to go to the Indies?

   Possible answers: The Indies were rich in gold, spices, and other goods. The Europeans wanted these riches.

2. How did Columbus get the king and queen of Spain to pay for his expedition?

   He convinced them that he could find a cheaper and quicker way to the Indies.

3. What are the names of the ships Columbus used in his first voyage?

   The Niña, Pinta, and Santa María

4. About how long did it take Columbus and his crew to cross the Atlantic?

   Approximately two months, nine days

5. What is the name of the place historians believe Columbus reached first?

   Bahama Islands

6. Why did Columbus lead more expeditions to the Americas, bringing with him people, animals, and other supplies?

   The Spanish wanted to find riches and start a colony that would bring profits.

7. How did the Columbian Exchange change the lives of the people involved?

   Possible answer: Both the Europeans and the Taino experienced new foods and animals. The Taino were exposed to germs their bodies could not fight, and many of them died. The settlers forced the Taino to give up their religious beliefs and their way of life.

Notes for Home: Your child learned about the effects of Columbus's voyages to the Americas.
Home Activity: Have your child explain how Columbus's voyages to the Americas affected people in Europe and the Americas.

36   Lesson Review   Workbook

© Scott Foresman 5

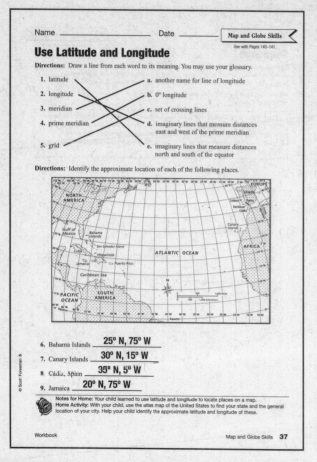

Map and Globe Skills
Use with Pages 140–141.

Use Latitude and Longitude

Directions: Draw a line from each word to its meaning. You may use your glossary.

1. latitude
2. longitude
3. meridian
4. prime meridian
5. grid

a. another name for line of longitude
b. 0° longitude
c. set of crossing lines
d. imaginary lines that measure distances east and west of the prime meridian
e. imaginary lines that measure distances north and south of the equator

Directions: Identify the approximate location of each of the following places.

6. Bahama Islands   25° N, 75° W
7. Canary Islands   30° N, 15° W
8. Cádiz, Spain   35° N, 5° W
9. Jamaica   20° N, 75° W

Notes for Home: Your child learned to use latitude and longitude to locate places on a map.
Home Activity: With your child, use the atlas map of the United States to find your state and the general location of your city. Help your child identify the approximate latitude and longitude of these.

Workbook   Map and Globe Skills   **37**

© Scott Foresman 5

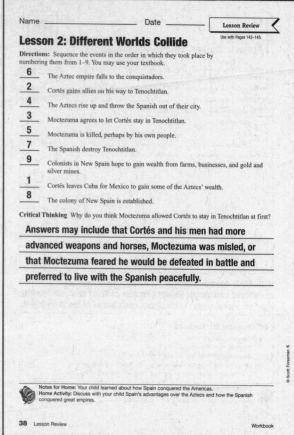

Lesson Review
Use with Pages 142–145.

Lesson 2: Different Worlds Collide

Directions: Sequence the events in the order in which they took place by numbering them from 1–9. You may use your textbook.

6 — The Aztec empire falls to the conquistadors.
2 — Cortés gains allies on his way to Tenochtitlan.
4 — The Aztecs rise up and throw the Spanish out of their city.
3 — Moctezuma agrees to let Cortés stay in Tenochtitlan.
5 — Moctezuma is killed, perhaps by his own people.
7 — The Spanish destroy Tenochtitlan.
9 — Colonists in New Spain hope to gain wealth from farms, businesses, and gold and silver mines.
1 — Cortés leaves Cuba for Mexico to gain some of the Aztecs' wealth.
8 — The colony of New Spain is established.

Critical Thinking Why do you think Moctezuma allowed Cortés to stay in Tenochtitlan at first?

Answers may include that Cortés and his men had more advanced weapons and horses, Moctezuma was misled, or that Moctezuma feared he would be defeated in battle and preferred to live with the Spanish peacefully.

Notes for Home: Your child learned about how Spain conquered the Americas.
Home Activity: Discuss with your child Spain's advantages over the Aztecs and how the Spanish conquered great empires.

38   Lesson Review   Workbook

© Scott Foresman 5

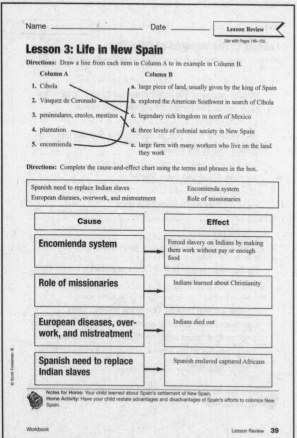

Lesson Review
Use with Pages 146–150.

Lesson 3: Life in New Spain

Directions: Draw a line from each item in Column A to its example in Column B.

Column A
1. Cibola
2. Vásquez de Coronado
3. peninsulares, creoles, mestizos
4. plantation
5. encomienda

Column B
a. large piece of land, usually given by the king of Spain
b. explored the American Southwest in search of Cibola
c. legendary rich kingdom in north of Mexico
d. three levels of colonial society in New Spain
e. large farm with many workers who live on the land they work

Directions: Complete the cause-and-effect chart using the terms and phrases in the box.

Spanish need to replace Indian slaves
European diseases, overwork, and mistreatment
Encomienda system
Role of missionaries

Cause	Effect
Encomienda system	Forced slavery on Indians by making them work without pay or enough food
Role of missionaries	Indians learned about Christianity
European diseases, overwork, and mistreatment	Indians died out
Spanish need to replace Indian slaves	Spanish enslaved captured Africans

Notes for Home: Your child learned about Spain's settlement of New Spain.
Home Activity: Have your child restate advantages and disadvantages of Spain's efforts to colonize New Spain.

Workbook   Lesson Review   **39**

© Scott Foresman 5

Vocabulary Review
Use with Chapter 4.

Vocabulary Review

Directions: Use vocabulary words from Chapter 4 to complete the crossword puzzle.

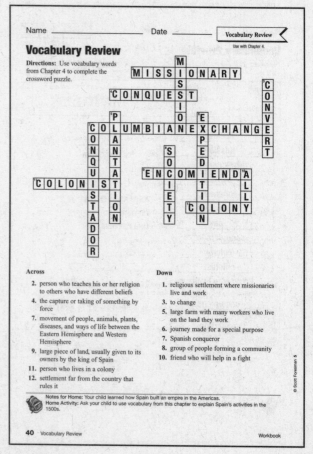

Across
2. person who teaches his or her religion to others who have different beliefs
4. the capture or taking of something by force
7. movement of people, animals, plants, diseases, and ways of life between the Eastern Hemisphere and Western Hemisphere
9. large piece of land, usually given to its owners by the king of Spain
11. person who lives in a colony
12. settlement far from the country that rules it

Down
1. religious settlement where missionaries live and work
3. to change
5. large farm with many workers who live on the land they work
6. journey made for a special purpose
7. Spanish conqueror
8. group of people forming a community
10. friend who will help in a fight

Notes for Home: Your child learned how Spain built an empire in the Americas.
Home Activity: Ask your child to use vocabulary from this chapter to explain Spain's activities in the 1500s.

40   Vocabulary Review   Workbook

© Scott Foresman 5

Vocabulary Preview

Directions: Write each vocabulary word from Chapter 5 beside its example or description. You may use your glossary.

charter	House of Burgesses	persecution	dissenter
stock	Northwest Passage	Mayflower Compact	proprietor
cash crop	Pilgrim	Puritan	debtor
indentured servant	Separatist		

1. Document that permitted colonists to settle on land claimed by their ruler ___ **charter**

2. Person who journeys for religious reasons ___ **Pilgrim**

3. A person whose views differ from others' ___ **dissenter**

4. Shares in a company often sold to raise money for the company ___ **stock**

5. Pilgrims' written plan of government for their colony ___ **Mayflower Compact**

6. Crop grown for profit ___ **cash crop**

7. Waterway connecting the Atlantic and Pacific Oceans ___ **Northwest Passage**

8. Person who owes money ___ **debtor**

9. Unjust treatment to a person because of his or her beliefs ___ **persecution**

10. A person who agreed to work for someone for a certain amount of time in exchange for the cost of the ocean voyage to North America ___ **indentured servant**

11. Group from England who wanted to purify, or reform, the Church of England ___ **Puritan**

12. Person who wanted to separate from the Church of England ___ **Separatist**

13. Owner ___ **proprietor**

14. The first law-making assembly in an English colony ___ **House of Burgesses**

Notes for Home: Your child learned about the struggle to found colonies in North America.
Home Activity: Ask your child to use new vocabulary from this chapter to tell you about the struggle people faced to found America's first colonies.

Lesson 1: Hard Times in Virginia

Directions: Identify the cause and effect in each chart. Label the items "Cause" or "Effect" in the spaces provided. Then draw an arrow between the boxes to show the correct direction. The first one has been done for you.

1. Cause	Effect
White returned to England seeking aid for the colonists in Roanoke. He arrived to find Spain and England at war and England with no ships to send supplies to the colonists.	White returned to Roanoke only to find that the colonists had mysteriously disappeared.

2. Cause	Effect
English ships were smaller than Spanish ships and could move faster. The English had more powerful guns than the Spanish.	The English won the Battle of the Spanish Armada and became one of the world's most powerful nations.

3. Effect	Cause
Jamestown settlers began to die almost as soon as they arrived.	Jamestown was located on low, swampy land where disease-carrying mosquitoes lived. The water was not healthy to drink.

4. Cause	Effect
The men at Jamestown spent their days searching for gold. They did not plant crops or build housing.	Men died of starvation and disease. John Smith took over, and under his guidance the colonists survived.

5. Effect	Cause
Jamestown grew rapidly.	Tobacco grew well in Virginia and became a cash crop as exports rose.

Notes for Home: Your child learned about the first English colonies in North America.
Home Activity: Have your child explain the causes and effects of events that took place during the early days at Roanoke and Jamestown.

Lesson 2: New European Colonies

Directions: The French and the Dutch settled colonies in North America. Classify terms that relate to the French and the Dutch by writing them in the appropriate columns.

beaver fur trading	Holland	New Netherland
Henry Hudson	Montreal	Quebec
Hudson River	New Amsterdam	Samuel de Champlain
Huron Indians	New France	St. Lawrence River

French	Dutch
Samuel de Champlain	**Henry Hudson**
New France	**New Netherland**
Quebec	**New Amsterdam**
Montreal	**Holland**
St. Lawrence River	**Hudson River**
Huron Indians	
beaver fur trading	

Directions: Suppose you are an explorer with Champlain or Hudson. Use one of the lists above to write a diary entry from your expedition.

Diary entries should reflect appropriate details from the selected expedition.

Notes for Home: Your child learned about French and Dutch settlements in North America.
Home Activity: Using the map on p. 166, trace the routes of the Champlain and Hudson expeditions with your child.

Lesson 3: The First Colonies

Directions: Answer the questions below about life in the first colonies in North America. You may use your textbook.

1. What was the reason the Pilgrims decided to flee England?

   They were seeking religious freedom.

2. Why did the Pilgrims go to Massachusetts and not Virginia?

   The Pilgrims were supposed to go to Virginia, but their ship went off course, and they ended up much farther north at Cape Cod.

3. How did the Pilgrims become friends with the Wampanoag?

   During the Pilgrims' first spring in New England, they were greeted in English by Samoset and taught where to fish and hunt and how to farm by Squanto.

4. How did Squanto, the interpreter for Massasoit and the Pilgrims, learn English?

   Squanto had been captured by European traders and sold into slavery. He escaped to England, where he learned English.

5. Why did the Pilgrims hold a celebration of thanksgiving?

   The Pilgrims were grateful for their first harvest and the help the Wampanoag had given them to survive their first year.

6. Why did the Puritans leave England, and what colony did they build in New England?

   They were seeking religious freedom; Massachusetts Bay Colony

Notes for Home: Your child learned about the Pilgrims' first thanksgiving and the reasons people left England to colonize North America.
Home Activity: With your child, discuss your family's Thanksgiving traditions and their meaning.

Fact and Opinion

A **fact** is a statement that can be checked. It can be proved to be true. An **opinion** is a personal view. It cannot be proved to be true or false.

Directions: Read the excerpts that follow. Look for facts and opinions. Underline the facts and circle the opinions.

> Samuel de Champlain sails his ship up the (mighty) St. Lawrence River, wondering where it will take him. He notes in his journal that this is (beautiful country, where there is good land covered with trees.")
>
> In 1621, Pilgrims and Native Americans celebrated a (delicious) feast of thanksgiving together.
>
> Philadelphia was the first colonial city to be planned on paper before it was built. Penn (wanted) the city to have wide streets, with (lots) of trees and green spaces.
>
> Today, Americans (believe) that people have the right to worship freely.

Directions: In the spaces provided, write one fact and one opinion about the Pilgrims' first winter.

Fact

Possible answer: Fact: The Pilgrims faced freezing weather, hunger, and disease.

Opinion

Opinion: The first winter was worse than the winters the Pilgrims had ever before experienced.

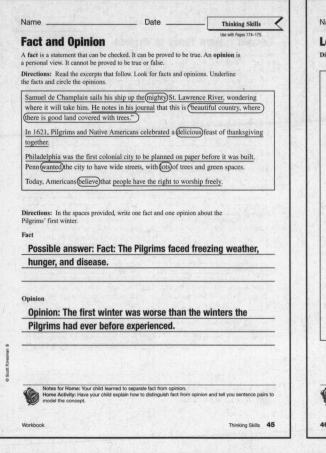

Notes for Home: Your child learned to separate fact from opinion.
Home Activity: Have your child explain how to distinguish fact from opinion and tell you sentence pairs to model the concept.

Workbook | Thinking Skills **45**

Lesson 4: The 13 English Colonies

Directions: Draw a line from each item in Column A to its description in Column B.

Column A	Column B
New England, Middle, and Southern Colonies	New York and New York City
Thick woods provided excellent timber for homes; coastal waters were rich in fish	The Middle Colonies
Breadbasket of the colonies	Dissenter forced by Puritans to leave Massachusetts; founder of Rhode Island
Rich soil produced valuable crops such as tobacco and rice	Georgia
Roger Williams	New England Colonies
England renamed New Netherland and New Amsterdam	Maryland
William Penn, a Quaker	The Southern Colonies
Large section of land north of Virginia, given to a Catholic landowner, for a colony	The three regions of the 13 Colonies
James Oglethorpe founded last English colony in North America with debtors; helped protect the Carolinas from the Spanish in Florida	Founder of Pennsylvania

Notes for Home: Your child learned about the geography of the 13 English colonies.
Home Activity: On a map of the eastern seaboard of the United States, locate with your child the sites of the 13 colonies.

46 Lesson Review | Workbook

Vocabulary Review

Directions: Use the terms in the box to complete each sentence with information from Chapter 5. You may use your textbook. Not all words will be used.

charter	Northwest Passage	Puritan
stock	Pilgrim	dissenter
cash crop	Separatist	proprietor
indentured servant	persecution	debtor
House of Burgesses	Mayflower Compact	

1. Tobacco was a **cash crop** in Virginia.
2. The **Mayflower Compact** called for just and equal laws for Plymouth.
3. Virginia's **House of Burgesses** was an important step toward self-government in the English colonies.
4. The company has sold 49 percent of its shares of **stock**.
5. The **Northwest Passage** was an imagined waterway connecting the Atlantic and Pacific Oceans.
6. Many settlers journeyed to North America to escape religious **persecution**.
7. Settlers received a **charter** from the king to settle the land.
8. Before landing the Mayflower, **Pilgrim** leaders wrote a plan of government for their colony.
9. Anne Hutchinson was a **dissenter** because her views were different from those of her leader.
10. A **proprietor** of a parcel of property can give or deny others permission to enter.

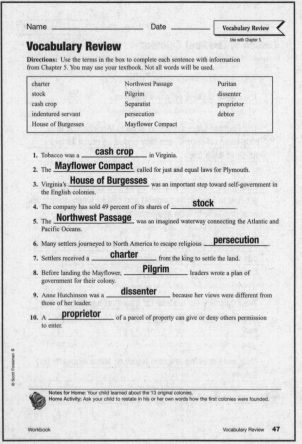

Notes for Home: Your child learned about the 13 original colonies.
Home Activity: Ask your child to restate in his or her own words how the first colonies were founded.

Workbook | Vocabulary Review **47**

UNIT 2 Project Breaking News

Use with Page 192.

Directions: A Native American and a European explorer or settler meet for the first time. In your group, assign roles and act out the meeting. Have the reporter give an eyewitness report of this historic event. Present your work to the class.

1. The Native American group we selected is _____
   The explorer's or settler's European country is _____
2. My role is (✔ one):
   ___ Native American ___ European explorer or settler ___ News reporter
3. The Native American's first impressions of the European explorer or settler:
   _____
   _____
4. The European settler's first impressions of the Native American:
   _____
   _____
5. The news reporter's description of the meeting:
   _____
   _____

Encourage students to use online or library resources to confirm that the first impressions they attribute to their Native American and European interviewees are factually accurate and avoid perpetrating stereotypes.

✔ Checklist for Students
___ We chose a Native American group from this unit.
___ We chose a European country of origin for the explorer or settler.
___ We wrote the first impressions of the Native American and European.
___ We wrote the news reporter's description.

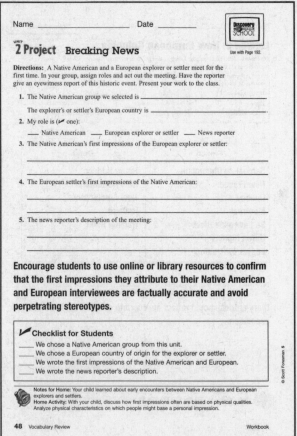

Notes for Home: Your child learned about early encounters between Native Americans and European explorers and settlers.
Home Activity: With your child, discuss how first impressions often are based on physical qualities. Analyze physical characteristics on which people might base a personal impression.

48 Vocabulary Review | Workbook

Panel 1 (Page 49)

Compare and Contrast

Directions: Read the passage. Use the reading strategy of compare and contrast to answer the questions below. Fill in the circle next to the correct answer.

Slavery was very important to the economies of the Northern and Southern Colonies. Although comparisons can be made between the life of slaves in the North and the South, there were differences, too.

In the South, few slaves worked in cities. Most worked on plantations. The planter often required enslaved people to work day and night. In spite of the difficult conditions, many slaves still found time for music. They built drums and other instruments similar to ones from their native countries in Africa. This kept their African culture alive.

Some West African slaves knew how to grow rice. Some shared this knowledge with plantation owners. For example, in the Carolinas rice became a valuable crop on many plantations.

Not all slaves in the Southern Colonies tended the crops. Some were skilled craftspeople who did carpentry work, tailoring, and blacksmithing on large plantations. They worked the same long, hard hours as those who worked in the fields.

The life of slaves in the Northern Colonies was in some ways different from life in the South. Some slaves worked on farms, but most worked in cities and towns. Most were not farmers. Instead, they worked as cooks or servants in people's homes, as skilled craftspeople, and in stores and inns. Some slaves in the North were able to earn extra money by taking on extra jobs. It sometimes took years of extra work at night, but some enslaved people earned enough money to buy their freedom.

1. How did slavery in the Southern Colonies differ from slavery in the Northern Colonies?
   - Ⓐ Slaves were owned by others.
   - Ⓑ Slaves had restrictions placed on them.
   - Ⓒ Families of slaves could be split up.
   - ● Most slaves worked on plantations.

2. In what ways was the life of enslaved people across America similar?
   - Ⓐ They worked night and day on farms.
   - Ⓑ They earned extra money by teaching planters to grow rice.
   - ● Slaves tried to keep up their African culture.
   - Ⓓ They cooked meals for people who lived in cities.

Notes for Home: Your child learned how to compare and contrast information.
Home Activity: With your child, compare and contrast your weekday activities. How does your child's day compare and contrast with yours?

Workbook   Reading Social Studies   **49**

Panel 2 (Page 50)

Vocabulary Preview

Directions: Match each vocabulary word to its meaning. Write the vocabulary word on the line after the definition. You may use your glossary.

apprentice	Middle Passage	Great Awakening
artisan	self-sufficient	almanac
triangular trade routes	town common	Stono Rebellion

1. A young person who learns a skill from a more experienced person
   apprentice

2. The second leg of a three-part voyage **Middle Passage**

3. A religious movement that revived many colonists' interest in religion
   Great Awakening

4. Routes shaped like giant triangles **triangular trade routes**

5. Reference book with facts and figures **almanac**

6. People who rely on themselves for most of what they need **self-sufficient**

7. An open space where sheep and cattle could graze **town common**

8. A skilled worker who makes things by hand **artisan**

9. Fight between enslaved people and owners near a river in South Carolina
   Stono Rebellion

Directions: On a separate sheet of a paper, write a paragraph comparing and contrasting life in the Northern and Southern English Colonies. Use as many of the vocabulary words as you can in your paragraph.

Same: Education and religion were important, farming was popular employment; Different: Enslaved people worked at different kinds of jobs, Southern plantations were larger than farms in the North.

Notes for Home: Your child learned about colonial life in the North American colonies.
Home Activity: Have your child use as many vocabulary words as possible to compare his or her life with that of a child in one of the original colonies.

50   Vocabulary Preview   Workbook

Panel 3 (Page 51)

Lesson 1: Working and Trading

Directions: Answer the following questions on the lines provided.

1. What were the advantages and disadvantages of being an apprentice?
   Advantages: great opportunity to train as an artisan, important responsibilities, good job potential; Disadvantages: long hours, hard work, little free time

2. What was the job of an artisan?
   An artisan was a skilled worker who made things by hand.

3. How did a person become an artisan?
   A person became an artisan by being a successful apprentice.

4. What was daily life like for children who grew up on farms during colonial times?
   Children who grew up on farms had just as much work to do as apprentices in towns and cities. From a very young age, children were given jobs on the farm such as gathering wood, serving food, and helping in the garden.

5. On what natural resources was the New England economy based? and the Southern economy? What industries developed?
   The New England economy was based on products from the forests and the sea. Industries included building, fishing, and whaling; The Southern economy was based on rich soil, warm weather, and ample rain. The main industry, farming, produced cash crops such as tobacco, rice, and indigo.

Notes for Home: Your child learned how people worked and traded during colonial times.
Home Activity: Ask your child if he or she would have preferred to have been an apprentice or a farm worker in colonial times. Have your child explain the duties and responsibilities of his or her choice.

Workbook   Lesson Review   **51**

Panel 4 (Page 52)

Read Newspapers

Newspapers are sources of news and events that are taking place now. They are usually printed daily or weekly. **News articles** are news stories based on facts about recent events. **Feature articles** have information about places, people, or events that would interest readers.

Directions: Label each topic as a news article or a feature article.

1. Movie reviews **Feature article**
2. Plane carrying emergency supplies lands safely **News article**
3. Ten worst traffic spots in metro area **Feature article**
4. Bridge opens to ease congestion **News article**
5. Movie star's wedding **Feature or news article**
6. Famous actor writes autobiography **Feature or news article**
7. Baby rescued by firefighters **News article**
8. Outdoor activities this weekend **Feature article**
9. Houses approved for the homeless **News article**
10. Historic building destroyed by flames **News article**
11. Presidential museum opens **News article**
12. Hay fever sufferers expect relief **Feature or news article**
13. Rising gas prices **News article**
14. Home remodeling tips **Feature article**
15. History of train exhibits **Feature article**

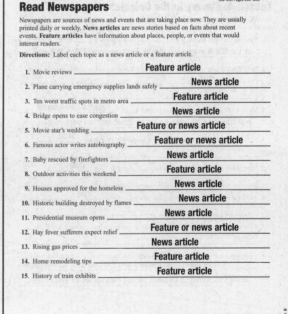

Notes for Home: Your child learned to identify the parts of a newspaper.
Home Activity: Look at a local newspaper with your child. As you skim it together, have your child classify stories as news or feature articles.

52   Reading and Writing Skills   Workbook

Lesson 2: Cities, Towns, and Farms

Directions: Match each term in the box to its description in the chart. Write the term in the second column in the chart.

Benjamin Franklin	Middle Colony towns	Puritans
Elizabeth Lucas Pinckney	general store	overseer
Southern plantation	town common	farming families
Philadelphia	meeting house	

Largest city in the 13 colonies	**Philadelphia**
Established first public library, hospital, and fire department in the 13 colonies	**Benjamin Franklin**
First planter to raise a successful crop of indigo	**Elizabeth Lucas Pinckney**
Began building towns in Massachusetts in 1630	**Puritans**
Open space where cattle and sheep could graze	**town common**
Plantation manager	**overseer**
Most important building in colonial town	**meeting house**
Served as marketplaces where farmers could sell their crops and buy tools and clothes	**Middle Colony towns**
Large farm where cash crops such as tobacco and rice were grown	**Southern plantation**
Place to buy imported goods such as tea and sugar	**general store**
Families who had to make or grow most of what they needed	**farming families**

Notes for Home: Your child learned about life in cities, towns, and on farms during colonial times.
Home Activity: Discuss with your child how colonial cities, towns, and farms compare with their modern-day counterparts.

Lesson 3: Everyday Life in the Colonies

Directions: Match the sentence fragments in Columns A and B to form complete sentences. Write the letter from Column B on the line in Column A.

Column A	Column B
1. Students learned the basics of reading, writing, arithmetic, and also learned the **E**	a. they were considered a waste of paper, expensive, and were hard to make.
2. When children were not at school, they spent a lot of time doing **C**	b. regions of the English Colonies.
3. Religion was an important part of life in all **B**	c. chores around their family's house or farm.
4. The Great Awakening, which revived many colonists' interest in religion, also **G**	d. common treats in the colonies, although all were not always tasty.
5. When the day's work was done, families often sat together and **F**	e. rules of polite behavior.
6. Letter writing was important; however, envelopes were not used because **A**	f. listened as a family member read aloud from a book.
7. Colonists learned to grow corn from Native Americans and **H**	g. inspired people to help others
8. Many desserts, such as donuts, ice cream, and fruit pies, were **D**	h. used it to make breads, puddings, and pancakes.

Notes for Home: Your child learned about daily life during colonial times.
Home Activity: Ask your child to contrast schools in colonial times with his or her typical school day.

Lesson 4: Slavery in the Colonies

Directions: Write True or False next to each statement. If the statement is false, rewrite it to make it true.

1. Slaves in the South worked in stores, inns, and as skilled artisans. **False; Slaves in the North worked in stores, inns, and as skilled artisans.**

2. In the North, slaves usually had more opportunities to improve their lives than did slaves in the South. **True**

3. Slaves could travel or go onto a ship in small groups. **False; Slaves could not travel or go onto a ship without written permission.**

4. In the South, most slaves were forced to work on large plantations. **True**

5. Some slaves showed planters how to raise rice, a valuable crop. **True**

6. Some slaves were expert carpenters, blacksmiths, or tailors. **True**

7. Slaves kept African culture alive by building drums, banjos, and other instruments. **True**

8. Plantation owners were afraid that slaves were using instruments to celebrate when a slave escaped. **False; Plantation owners were afraid that slaves were using instruments to send secret messages to each other.**

Notes for Home: Your child learned about the lives of slaves.
Home Activity: Ask your child how he or she would like to be treated by others.

Vocabulary Review

Directions: Circle the term in parentheses that best completes each sentence. You may use your glossary.

1. The (almanac, (Great Awakening,) Middle Passage) caused many colonists to become interested in religion once again and to help others.

2. A skilled worker, such as a carpenter or blacksmith, was an (apprentice, almanac, (artisan)).

3. The trade route from New England to West Africa to the West Indies and back to New England was a (Middle Passage, Stono Rebellion, (triangular trade route)).

4. A young person would spend years as an (almanac, (apprentice,) artisan), learning a skill from a more experienced person.

5. In colonial times people read ((almanacs,) apprentices, town commons), or reference books with facts and figures, for their valuable information.

6. The (Great Awakening, (Stono Rebellion,) triangular trade routes) took place when slaves clashed with their owners near a river in South Carolina.

7. The open space where sheep and cattle could graze in a town was known as the (triangular trade route, (town common,) Middle Passage).

8. The second leg of a three-part voyage was known as the ((Middle Passage,) Great Awakening, Stono Rebellion).

9. The New England Colonies were (triangular trade routes, apprentices, (self-sufficient))—they relied on themselves for most of what they needed.

Directions: Describe the work life of a slave or an apprentice in the early English Colonies. Use as many vocabulary words as you can in your summary.

Students' descriptions should correctly apply terms shown above and be supported by details from Chapter 6.

Notes for Home: Your child learned new terms related to life in colonial times.
Home Activity: With your child, discuss how people in colonial days tried to become self-sufficient. Discuss whether or not this goal is possible in today's society.

© Scott Foresman 5

Vocabulary Preview

Use with Chapter 7.

Directions: Read each sentence. Write a synonym or description for the underlined word on the line provided. You may use your glossary.

1. Wealthy ranchers in New Mexico built haciendas. **Large estates**

2. The soldiers held watch at the presidio. **Military fort**

3. Travelers followed El Camino Real between Mexico City and Santa Fe.
"The Royal Road"; It connected Mexico City and Santa Fe.

4. The Pueblo fought intensely in the Pueblo Revolt.
Fighting led by the Pueblo against the Spanish in New Mexico

5. Beaver furs were exchanged for other goods at the trading post.
Place where French and Native Americans met to trade goods

6. The Allegheny is a tributary of the Ohio River.
Stream or river that flows into a larger river

7. King Philip's War took place in New England. **War between the English and a Wampanoag leader named Metacom, known as "King Philip"**

8. Many families moved to the backcountry so they could have their own land.
Rugged stretch of frontier land near the Appalachian Mountains

9. The British won the French and Indian War. **War between Britain and France over lands in North America**

10. Many British died in Pontiac's Rebellion. **Ottawa's fight against the British along the Ohio River valley and the Great Lakes**

11. The King hoped that the Proclamation of 1763 would prevent further battles with the Native Americans. **Colonists were no longer allowed to settle on land west of the Appalachian Mountains.**

Notes for Home: Your child learned terms to describe the struggle for control of North America in the 1600s.
Home Activity: Have your child restate the reasons for these conflicts, using as many vocabulary words as possible.

Lesson 1: The Spanish Move North

Use with Pages 232–236.

Directions: Circle the term in parentheses that best completes each sentence. You may use your textbook.

1. The capital of New Spain was (Mexico City,) Santa Fe).

2. In 1565, Pedro Menendez de Avilés led a small fleet of (British, (Spanish)) warships to Florida.

3. After a series of bloody battles between the ((French,) British) and the Spanish, Florida became part of New Spain.

4. After moving into Florida, the Spanish expanded into a region they called New Mexico. The town of (St. Augustine, (Santa Fe)) was founded and named the capital.

5. The Spanish hoped to find (cattle ranches, (gold and silver)) in New Mexico.

6. Spanish ranchers grazed ((cattle,) horses) on the grasses of the haciendas.

7. New Mexico was connected to Mexico City by ((El Camino Real,) the Rio Grande).

8. In 1680, a Pueblo leader named ((Popé,) Junípero Serra) led a revolt against the Spanish in New Mexico.

9. The white cross the Pueblo leader, Juan, carried to Santa Fe meant ((surrender,) battle).

10. In the fighting that became known as the Pueblo Revolt, the (Pueblo, (Spanish)) were driven out of New Mexico.

11. By 1692, the ((Spanish,) Pueblo) were able to recapture New Mexico.

12. The Spanish founded ((San Antonio,) St. Augustine) in 1718.

13. Father Junípero Serra founded Spanish (presidios, (missions)) in another part of New Spain, California.

Notes for Home: Your child learned about the Spanish struggle to take over North America.
Home Activity: Role-play the Pueblo Revolt with your child. Help him or her identify the points of view of the Spanish and the Pueblo.

Lesson 2: French Explore the Mississippi

Use with Pages 240–243.

Directions: Complete each sentence by copying the best ending from the box onto the lines provided.

> he wanted to reach the mouth of the Mississippi River.
>
> he made a map of the river and kept a journal of the experience.
>
> it has an ideal location near the mouth of the Mississippi River.
>
> control of the river would help them reach new lands where they could build trading posts.
>
> he realized the river could not be the long-sought Northwest Passage because it continued to flow south.

1. The leaders of New France wanted to explore the Mississippi because
control of the river would help them reach new lands where they could build trading posts.

2. After traveling some 1,000 miles down the Mississippi, Marquette decided to return home because **he realized the river could not be the long-sought Northwest Passage because it continued to flow south.**

3. Today we have an idea of some of the details of Marquette's journey down the Mississippi because **he made a map of the river and kept a journal of the experience.**

4. La Salle was willing to carry his canoe over snow and frozen streams because
he wanted to reach the mouth of the Mississippi River.

5. New Orleans became a busy trading center because **it has an ideal location near the mouth of the Mississippi River.**

Notes for Home: Your child learned about the French exploration of the Mississippi River.
Home Activity: With your child, discuss the hardships explorers like Marquette and Jolliet faced on their voyages of discovery.

Compare Maps at Different Scales

Use with Pages 244–245.

In Chapter 5, you learned about the French colony of Montreal, in the present-day province of Quebec.

Directions: Answer the following questions on the lines provided.

Small-Scale Map

Large-Scale Map

1. Which map would you use to measure the distance from Montreal to Laval?
small scale

2. Which map would you use to locate McGill University?
large scale

3. About how far is it from Montreal to Longueuil—1 mile, 3 miles, or 20 miles?
about 3 miles

4. What large road is near the Planetarium and the Convention Center?
Route 720

Notes for Home: Your child learned to compare maps at different scales.
Home Activity: With your child, compare the areas shown by a standard road map (small scale) to a map of your neighborhood or subdivision (large scale). Discuss when it is best to use each map.

Lesson 3: The French and Indian War

Use with Pages 246-251.

Directions: Complete the cause-and-effect chart with information from your textbook.

Cause	Effect
English settlers wanted more land to build towns and farms. They began moving west.	**Native Americans resisted English settlement.**
The English settlers were willing to fight for the land they wanted.	**In New England, the conflict over land led to war in 1675.**
After a year of fighting, the leader of the Native Americans, Metacom, was killed.	The English settlers won the war and gained control of most of New England.
By the mid-1700s, settlers moved as far west as the Ohio River valley—a region claimed by both France and Great Britain.	**The French refused to leave. They and their American Indian allies went to war with Great Britain.**
British General James Wolfe captured Quebec, the capital of New France, in September 1759.	The victory helped the British win the French and Indian War.

Notes for Home: Your child learned about the causes and effects of the French and Indian War.
Home Activity: To practice this skill with your child, identify several cause-and-effect relationships around your home.

Vocabulary Review

Use with Chapter 7.

Directions: Use the clues from the chapter to complete the crossword puzzle.

hacienda
presidio
El Camino Real
Pueblo Revolt
trading post
tributary
King Philip's War
backcountry
French and Indian War
Pontiac's Rebellion
Proclamation of 1763

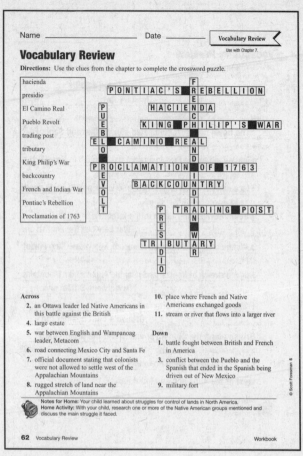

Across

2. an Ottawa leader led Native Americans in this battle against the British
4. large estate
5. war between English and Wampanoag leader, Metacom
6. road connecting Mexico City and Santa Fe
7. official document stating that colonists were not allowed to settle west of the Appalachian Mountains
8. rugged stretch of land near the Appalachian Mountains
10. place where French and Native Americans exchanged goods
11. stream or river that flows into a larger river

Down

1. battle fought between British and French in America
3. conflict between the Pueblo and the Spanish that ended in the Spanish being driven out of New Mexico
9. military fort

Notes for Home: Your child learned about struggles for control of lands in North America.
Home Activity: With your child, research one or more of the Native American groups mentioned and discuss the main struggle it faced.

---

3 Project Colonial Living

Use with Page 258.

Directions: In a game show, see if your classmates can guess your colonial occupation. Then try to guess the other students' occupations.

1. My occupation is _____

2. Clues about my colonial occupation (in sentence form):

   A. _____
   B. _____
   C. _____
   D. _____
   E. _____

3. Questions to ask other students to identify their colonial occupations:

   _____
   _____
   _____
   _____

As needed, review the occupations and the clues students select. Encourage them to provide clues that hint at, but do not reveal, the occupation.

✔ **Checklist for Students**

_____ I chose an occupation from colonial times.
_____ I researched five statements of fact as clues about my occupation and wrote them on an index card.
_____ I wrote questions to guess other colonial occupations.
_____ I participated in the class game show.

Notes for Home: Your child learned about occupations in colonial America.
Home Activity: Review the Fact File list of colonial occupations in Unit 3 of your child's textbook. Together, identify jobs available today that did not exist hundreds of years ago.

Cause and Effect

Use with Pages 264-265.

Sometimes writers use clue words such as *because, so,* or *since* to signal cause and effect. A cause may have more than one effect, and an effect may have more than one cause.

Directions: Read the following passage. Use the reading strategy of cause and effect to answer the questions. Fill in the circle next to the correct answer.

The American Revolution at Sea

Many of the battles fought during the American Revolution were fought on land, but battles were also fought at sea. The British controlled the seas. They were expected to defeat the colonists since they had a large naval fleet and the colonies did not. In the colonies, ships from the Continental Navy, along with ships from the colonies' own navy, managed to capture or sink a number of British ships. They were able to do this because they had the help of private ships, known as privateers.

The number of privateers grew during the years of the revolution, so these ships were able to cause significant damage to the British fleet. Because the privateers were spread out in the Atlantic as far as the West Indies and British Isles, their actions also hurt Britain by affecting its trade.

In 1778 the French and the American colonies formed an alliance, and Spain entered the war as an ally of France. Because of this alliance, Britain could no longer control the seas. A British fleet was always kept on guard against invasion in the English Channel. This left vast areas unguarded, so the Spanish and French naval forces were able to attack wherever they pleased.

1. What caused people to expect the British to defeat the colonists at sea?
   Ⓐ Britain's allies
   Ⓑ Britain's wealth
   ● Britain's large navy
   Ⓓ King George's political influence

2. What effect did the privateers have on the British fleet?
   Ⓐ They were in the way of the Continental Navy.
   Ⓑ They helped defeat the Continental Navy.
   ● They helped defeat the British fleet.
   Ⓓ They grew to the size of the British fleet.

3. What effect did Spain's and France's alliances with the American colonies have on the British?
   Ⓐ It made them stronger.
   ● It made them lose control of the seas.
   Ⓒ It gave them more allies.
   Ⓓ It expanded their naval fleet.

Notes for Home: Your child learned to apply the reading strategy of cause and effect to a passage.
Home Activity: With your child, read a newspaper article or editorial and list the causes and effects that you find.

T16 Answer Key   Workbook

Vocabulary Preview

Directions: Match each vocabulary word to its meaning. Write the vocabulary word on the line provided. Not all words will be used. You may use your glossary.

Parliament	Daughters of Liberty	Loyalist
Stamp Act	Boston Massacre	First Continental Congress
repeal	Committee of Correspondence	militia
Sons of Liberty	Tea Act	minutemen
Townshend Acts	Boston Tea Party	American Revolution
tariff	Intolerable Acts	Battle of Bunker Hill
boycott	Patriot	

1. **Townshend Acts** — laws calling for a tax on imported goods
2. **tariff** — a tax on imported goods
3. **Stamp Act** — law that placed a tax on printed materials in the colonies
4. **repeal** — to cancel
5. **Patriot** — a colonist who opposed British rule
6. **Battle of Bunker Hill** — important revolutionary battle that took place on Breed's Hill
7. **Tea Act** — law that allowed only one company to sell tea to the colonists
8. **Intolerable Acts** — new laws dictated by Britain to punish the colonists for the Boston Tea Party
9. **Sons of Liberty** — group that led protests against the new Stamp Act tax
10. **militia** — a volunteer army
11. **Parliament** — Britain's law-making assembly
12. **minutemen** — militia groups who could be ready to fight for their colony at only a minute's notice
13. **American Revolution** — a war Americans fought for independence
14. **Boston Tea Party** — when colonists dumped tea into Boston Harbor to protest the Tea Act

Notes for Home: Your child learned about troubles between the British and the colonies.
Home Activity: Have your child write each vocabulary word on the front of a small piece of paper and the definition on the back. Lay out these cards with the vocabulary terms face up. Then make a second set with definitions only. Lay out these cards face up. Have your child match each term with its definition.

Lesson 1: Trouble over Taxes

Directions: Match each cause to its effect to complete each sentence. Then circle the clue words that signal cause and effect.

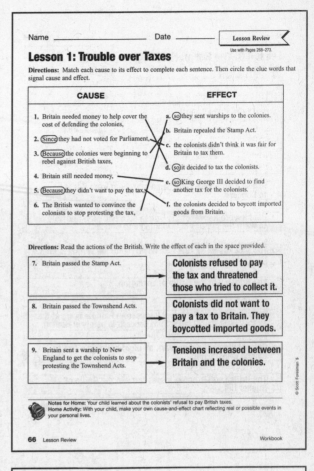

CAUSE	EFFECT
1. Britain needed money to help cover the cost of defending the colonies,	a. (so) they sent warships to the colonies.
2. (Since) they had not voted for Parliament,	b. Britain repealed the Stamp Act.
3. (Because) the colonies were beginning to rebel against British taxes,	c. the colonists didn't think it was fair for Britain to tax them.
4. Britain still needed money,	d. (so) it decided to tax the colonists.
5. (Because) they didn't want to pay the tax,	e. (so) King George III decided to find another tax for the colonists.
6. The British wanted to convince the colonists to stop protesting the tax,	f. the colonists decided to boycott imported goods from Britain.

Directions: Read the actions of the British. Write the effect of each in the space provided.

7. Britain passed the Stamp Act.	→	Colonists refused to pay the tax and threatened those who tried to collect it.
8. Britain passed the Townshend Acts.	→	Colonists did not want to pay a tax to Britain. They boycotted imported goods.
9. Britain sent a warship to New England to get the colonists to stop protesting the Townshend Acts.	→	Tensions increased between Britain and the colonies.

Notes for Home: Your child learned about the colonists' refusal to pay British taxes.
Home Activity: With your child, make your own cause-and-effect chart reflecting real or possible events in your personal lives.

Lesson 2: The Colonists Rebel

Directions: Answer the questions below on the lines provided. You may use your textbook.

1. What was the Boston Massacre?

British soldiers fired into a Boston crowd, killing five people.

2. Why did Parliament repeal the Townshend Acts?

because the colonial boycott was hurting British businesses

3. Why did Parliament decide to keep the tax on tea?

British leaders wanted to show the colonists that they still had the right to tax the colonies.

4. Who was Paul Revere?

He was a silversmith and one of the express riders for the Committees of Correspondence.

5. What two goals did the British hope to accomplish by passing the Tea Act?

The British hoped to help the struggling East India Company and to get the colonists to pay taxes to Britain.

6. How did the colonists respond to the Tea Act?

The colonists protested the Tea Act and dumped British tea into Boston Harbor.

7. Why did Britain pass new laws that the colonists referred to as the Intolerable Acts?

as punishment for the Boston Tea Party

Notes for Home: Your child learned why the colonists protested British taxation.
Home Activity: With your child, discuss this lesson. Then have your child write the main idea of the lesson on a large self-stick note. Have him or her write supporting details on smaller self-stick notes and place them around the perimeter of the main-idea note.

Use Primary Sources

Primary sources are eyewitness accounts of history. They give you firsthand knowledge about how things were at the time of the event. They are made by people who participated in the event being described. Primary sources can be letters, diaries, documents, speeches, interviews, photographs, paintings, or newspapers. Many of the pictures in this chapter of your textbook are photographs of primary sources.

Directions: The primary source below relates to the Boston Massacre. Study the source and answer the questions that follow.

1. What is taking place in this picture?

British soldiers are firing on protesting colonists.

2. Why do you think the incident was referred to as a "massacre"? What does this picture tell you about how the British soldiers responded to colonists who protested during revolutionary times?

Possible responses might include: The British soldiers responded with violent actions.

Notes for Home: Your child learned to identify and study primary sources.
Home Activity: With your child, examine postcards or letters from family or friends. Describe what about the wording identifies the item as a primary source. Then identify the person's perspective on the events being described.

Lesson 3: The Revolution Begins

Directions: Complete the sequence chart by writing the sentences in the box in the order in which they took place. You may use your textbook.

- British soldiers secretly begin marching from Boston to Concord.
- British soldiers suffer heavy losses from Patriots firing at them as they walk the 20 miles from Concord to safety in Boston.
- Colonel Prescott's men work all night building a fort to defend Breed's Hill.
- Paul Revere knows of the British soldiers' plan and sets out to warn the militias in Lexington and Concord.
- The British win the Battle of Lexington.
- The British suffer heavy losses but win the Battle of Bunker Hill.
- The shot known as "the shot heard round the world" is fired.

1. **British soldiers secretly begin marching from Boston to Concord.**

2. **Paul Revere knows of the British soldiers' plan and sets out to warn the militias in Lexington and Concord.**

3. **The shot known as "the shot heard round the world" is fired.**

4. **The British win the Battle of Lexington.**

5. **British soldiers suffer heavy losses from Patriots firing at them as they walk the 20 miles from Concord to safety in Boston.**

6. **Colonel Prescott's men work all night building a fort to defend Breed's Hill.**

7. **The British suffer heavy losses but win the Battle of Bunker Hill.**

Notes for Home: Your child learned the events that led to the American Revolution.
Home Activity: Discuss with your child ways countries can try to resolve conflicts without going to war.

Vocabulary Review

Directions: Choose the vocabulary term from the box that best completes each sentence. Not all words will be used. Write the term on the line provided.

Parliament	Daughters of Liberty	Loyalist
Stamp Act	Boston Massacre	First Continental Congress
repeal	Committee of Correspondence	militia
Sons of Liberty	Tea Act	minutemen
Townshend Acts	Boston Tea Party	American Revolution
tariff	Intolerable Acts	Battle of Bunker Hill
boycott	Patriot	

1. The government decided to _____**repeal**_____, or cancel, the law.

2. Local merchants held a _____**boycott**_____ against imported goods.

3. The **Intolerable Acts** were laws punishing the colonists for dumping tea into Boston Harbor.

4. Even today, **Parliament** continues to be the law-making assembly for Great Britain.

5. The **Stamp Act** required all colonists to pay a tax on printed materials.

6. The **First Continental Congress** was formed by representatives of all but one of the 13 colonies. Representatives voted on what action to take against the British and their taxes.

7. The **Townshend Acts** were laws requiring a tax be paid on imported goods.

8. The killing of five men in Boston by panicked British soldiers is known as the **Boston Massacre**.

9. The British lost many soldiers in the **Battle of Bunker Hill**, which actually took place on Breed's Hill.

10. The **Daughters of Liberty** supported the boycott of imported goods by making tea from herbs and berries and by weaving cloth.

Notes for Home: Your child learned about how the American Revolution began.
Home Activity: Have your child draw a picture representing the American Revolution period and have him or her explain the picture using as many vocabulary words as possible.

Vocabulary Preview

Directions: Find the meaning of each vocabulary term from Chapter 9. Write the meaning on the lines provided. You may use your glossary.

Second Continental Congress **second meeting of American leaders who made decisions for the colonies and formed a Continental Army**

Continental Army **an army with soldiers from all 13 colonies; formed by the Second Continental Congress**

Olive Branch Petition **a petition from Congress to King George III that asked for more freedom for the colonists to govern themselves**

Declaration of Independence **a document stating why the colonies wanted independence**

traitor **a person who works against his or her country**

Green Mountain Boys **Patriot soldiers from Vermont, led by Ethan Allen**

mercenary **a soldier from one country paid to fight for another country**

Battle of Saratoga **a battle fought between the Americans and the British; turning point of the American Revolution**

Treaty of Paris **the treaty that officially ended the American Revolution; Great Britain recognized the United States of America as an independent nation**

Notes for Home: Your child learned about the American Revolution.
Home Activity: Help your child learn the terms and their meanings by using each term in a sentence.

Lesson 1: Declaring Independence

Directions: Put the events in the sequence chart in the correct order. Number the events from 1 (earliest) to 10 (latest). Write the numbers on the blank lines before the boxes.

6 | Thomas Paine publishes *Common Sense*.

4 | Congress attempts to avoid war by sending a petition to King George III.

2 | The Continental Army is formed.

3 | George Washington agrees to command the army.

8 | The Declaration of Independence is signed by the members of Congress.

5 | King George wants to "put a speedy end" to the illegal rebellion in the colonies.

1 | The Second Continental Congress is held.

7 | Congress decides to vote for independence.

Notes for Home: Your child learned about Congress's decision to declare independence.
Home Activity: With your child, write a cause and effect for each event in this lesson on a separate slip of paper. Cut apart each cause and effect. Mix up the slips of paper and have your child put them back in the correct sequence.

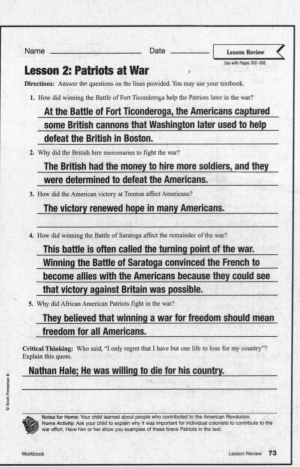

Lesson 2: Patriots at War

Directions: Answer the questions on the lines provided. You may use your textbook.

1. How did winning the Battle of Fort Ticonderoga help the Patriots later in the war?

   At the Battle of Fort Ticonderoga, the Americans captured some British cannons that Washington later used to help defeat the British in Boston.

2. Why did the British hire mercenaries to fight the war?

   The British had the money to hire more soldiers, and they were determined to defeat the Americans.

3. How did the American victory at Trenton affect Americans?

   The victory renewed hope in many Americans.

4. How did winning the Battle of Saratoga affect the remainder of the war?

   This battle is often called the turning point of the war. Winning the Battle of Saratoga convinced the French to become allies with the Americans because they could see that victory against Britain was possible.

5. Why did African American Patriots fight in the war?

   They believed that winning a war for freedom should mean freedom for all Americans.

Critical Thinking: Who said, "I only regret that I have but one life to lose for my country"? Explain this quote.

   Nathan Hale; He was willing to die for his country.

Notes for Home: Your child learned about people who contributed to the American Revolution.
Home Activity: Ask your child to explain why it was important for individual colonists to contribute to the war effort. Have him or her show you examples of these brave Patriots in the text.

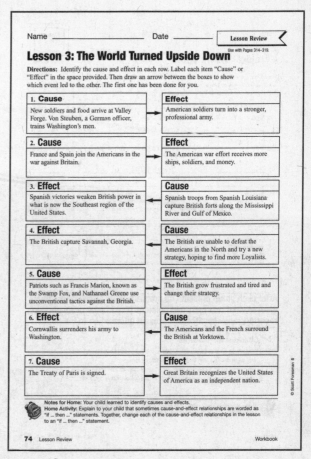

Lesson 3: The World Turned Upside Down

Directions: Identify the cause and effect in each row. Label each item "Cause" or "Effect" in the space provided. Then draw an arrow between the boxes to show which event led to the other. The first one has been done for you.

1. Cause New soldiers and food arrive at Valley Forge. Von Steuben, a German officer, trains Washington's men.	**Effect** American soldiers turn into a stronger, professional army.
2. Cause France and Spain join the Americans in the war against Britain.	**Effect** The American war effort receives more ships, soldiers, and money.
3. Effect Spanish victories weaken British power in what is now the Southeast region of the United States.	**Cause** Spanish troops from Spanish Louisiana capture British forts along the Mississippi River and Gulf of Mexico.
4. Effect The British capture Savannah, Georgia.	**Cause** The British are unable to defeat the Americans in the North and try a new strategy, hoping to find more Loyalists.
5. Cause Patriots such as Francis Marion, known as the Swamp Fox, and Nathanael Greene use unconventional tactics against the British.	**Effect** The British grow frustrated and tired and change their strategy.
6. Effect Cornwallis surrenders his army to Washington.	**Cause** The Americans and the French surround the British at Yorktown.
7. Cause The Treaty of Paris is signed.	**Effect** Great Britain recognizes the United States of America as an independent nation.

Notes for Home: Your child learned to identify causes and effects.
Home Activity: Explain to your child that sometimes cause-and-effect relationships are worded as "if ... then ..." statements. Together, change each of the cause-and-effect relationships in the lesson to an "if ... then ..." statement.

Make Generalizations

A generalization is a broad statement or idea about a subject. It explains how different facts might have an important idea in common. Generalizations help explain the big picture and make it easier to remember many different facts.

Directions: Read the following passage and answer the questions on the lines provided.

The American Revolution was a long-lasting and difficult battle for independence. Although this war often is portrayed as being fought entirely by men, this is not true. Women contributed to the war effort in a number of ways.

The struggle for independence was not limited to battles on the battlefield. It included caring for the soldiers as well as providing funding to keep the effort going. For a time, Washington's army struggled because it had insufficient food and inadequate clothing for protection from the elements. George Washington's wife, Martha, and many other women prepared food for the soldiers and cared for the wounded.

These patriotic women reasoned that independence was for everybody, not just for the soldiers. Martha Washington and other women sewed and mended the soldiers' clothing. They also knitted socks for the soldiers, who often had gone barefoot in battle and in the snow, risking their health and their lives.

History also tells of women participating on the battlefield. One story tells of a woman who joined the army under a man's name. She fought in numerous battles and was wounded twice before her secret was revealed. Another woman reportedly took her husband's place in battle after his death.

Published writings also helped support the war effort. Women wrote and published songs and other works in an effort to boost soldiers' morale and increase public awareness. The better informed people were, the more likely they were to support the war effort with money and various types of volunteer service.

1. Which sentence tells you the main idea of the passage? **Women contributed to the war effort in a number of ways.**

2. Which sentence in the passage is a generalization? **Possible answer: Women contributed to the war effort in a number of ways.**

3. What generalization can you make about the passage? **Possible Answer: Women played an important role in the American Revolution.**

Notes for Home: Your child learned how to make generalizations.
Home Activity: With your child, practice making both true and false generalizations about events in your daily lives. Discuss what types of mistakes lead to false generalizations.

Vocabulary Review

Directions: Match each vocabulary term from Chapter 9 to its cause, clue, or definition. Write the term in the space provided.

Second Continental Congress	Declaration of Independence	mercenary
Continental Army	traitor	Battle of Saratoga
Olive Branch Petition	Green Mountain Boys	Treaty of Paris

1. **Treaty of Paris** — Great Britain recognizes the United States of America as an independent nation.

2. **Second Continental Congress** — Colonial militias clashing with British soldiers at Concord and Lexington cause American leaders to meet and make many decisions.

3. **mercenary** — Determined to win the war against the Americans, King George hires German soldiers to fight for Britain.

4. **Continental Army** — This was necessary for America to defend itself against the British army.

5. **Battle of Saratoga** — Britain attempts to take control of Lake Champlain and the Hudson River.

6. **Declaration of Independence** — Congress prepares a document in an effort to gain every colony's support. The document explains the Americans' reasons for breaking with Britain.

7. **Green Mountain Boys** — This was a group of Patriot soldiers from Vermont, led by Ethan Allen.

8. **Olive Branch Petition** — Congress offers a peaceful solution to the problem with Britain.

9. **traitor** — Benedict Arnold fights for the British in exchange for money.

Notes for Home: Your child learned about events of the American Revolution.
Home Activity: With your child, examine each of the given causes, clues, and definitions and underline key words. Encourage your child to use these key words to remember the meanings of the chapter 9 vocabulary terms.

Top-left worksheet

Name _____ Date _____

Discovery SCHOOL

4 Project   News Then

Use with Page 328.

Directions: In a group, present a news program about an event described in this unit from the 1760s or during the American Revolution. Group members should choose a role and complete the assignment for that role.

1. The event is _____

2. My role in the news program is (✔ one):

_____ News anchor   _____ Reporter   _____ Eyewitness

3. News Anchor
Write a summary of the event. Describe the people involved, details about their role, and the outcome or importance of the event.

_____

_____

4. Reporter
Write questions (and answers) on behalf of the eyewitnesses to the event. Ask them who was involved, what the people did, and what they think is the outcome or importance of the event.

_____

_____

5. Eyewitness
If you are an eyewitness, write a description of what you saw. Include the names of the people involved, what they did, and the outcome or importance of the event.

After each group presents its program, have audience members discuss what role facts and opinions play in how news anchors, reporters, and eyewitnesses present information to the public.

✔ **Checklist for Students**

_____ We chose an event from the 1760s or the American Revolution.
_____ We each chose a role to play in the news program.
_____ We wrote about the event from the point of view of our assigned role.
_____ Our group made a banner and background for our news program.

Notes for Home: Your child learned about events of the late 1700s.
Home Activity: With your child, watch a news program about national events. Discuss the roles reporters, news anchors, and eyewitnesses play in sharing a news event with TV viewers.

Top-right worksheet

Name _____ Date _____

Reading Social Studies

Draw Conclusions

Use with Pages 334–335.

Directions: Read the information below. Then fill in the circle next to the correct answer.

The French Revolution took place at about the same time as the American Revolution. Both countries were trying to achieve a democratic form of government. One major difference, however, was that the French already had a government in place.

During the course of the French Revolution, the existing French government would be completely destroyed. The majority of French citizens were dissatisfied with it and would not rest until it was changed.

At that time, the French government was led by a king, and citizens belonged to different social classes. Benefits and privileges were given to some according to their social class. For instance, some classes did not have to pay taxes and were allowed to collect dues from the poorer classes.

Another factor leading to the French Revolution was a lack of money. France had just helped the United States battle Britain in the American Revolution, and now it needed money. France already taxed some of its people, but now the situation called for additional taxes. Representatives of the king decided to begin taxing *all* landowners. This unpopular action caused the people to rebel against their government and resist what they considered to be unfair treatment.

Violent protests took place throughout the country. Poorer citizens fought for their own rights and to keep the wealthy from receiving special privileges.

Before the end of the French Revolution, the existing social divisions were outlawed. However, France's problems were far from over.

1. Which statement supports the conclusion that the American Revolution helped spark the French Revolution?
   Ⓐ The French government was ruled by a king.
   Ⓑ French citizens belonged to different social classes.
   ● France had just helped the Americans battle Britain in the American Revolution.
   Ⓓ There was a great deal of civil unrest in France.

2. Which statement supports the conclusion that the majority of French people wanted a new form of government?
   ● Poorer citizens fought for their rights and to keep the wealthy from receiving special privileges.
   Ⓑ Money was one cause of the French Revolution.
   Ⓒ Privileges were determined by social class.
   Ⓓ France already taxed some of its people.

Notes for Home: Your child learned how to draw conclusions about a historical event.
Home Activity: With your child, brainstorm a list of facts about the American Revolution and another list of facts about the French Revolution. Together, draw conclusions about how the Americans may have influenced the French citizenry to rebel against their government.

Bottom-left worksheet

Name _____ Date _____

Vocabulary Preview

Vocabulary Preview

Use with Chapter 10.

Directions: Match each vocabulary term to its definition. Write the number of the term in the space provided. Not all terms will be used. You may use your glossary.

1. Articles of Confederation — **2**
2. ratify — **19**
3. legislative branch
4. executive branch — **7**
5. judicial branch — **9**
6. inflation — **12**
7. Shays' Rebellion
8. Northwest Ordinance — **25**
9. delegate — **6**
10. Constitutional Convention — **13**
11. Virginia Plan
12. New Jersey Plan — **15**
13. compromise
14. Great Compromise — **23**
15. Three-Fifths Compromise — **10**
16. Preamble — **3**
17. reserved powers — **21**
18. separation of powers
19. checks and balances — **11**
20. veto
21. Federalists — **4**
22. federal — **18**
23. Antifederalists
24. *The Federalist* — **1**
25. amendment — **20**
26. Bill of Rights — **8**
                                — **22**

a. to approve something
b. system to guard against any one branch of the government becoming too powerful
c. movement by farmers to protest high taxes
d. a representative
e. plan that proposed that each state, regardless of size, would have the same number of representatives in Congress
f. an addition or change to the Constitution
g. happens when prices rise very quickly
h. each side gives up something to reach an agreement
i. three out of every five slaves would be counted for population and taxation
j. group of people who were not happy with the Constitution
k. assembly that replaced the Articles of Confederation
l. the part of the government that passes laws
m. formerly nationalist group that wanted a strong national government
n. plan that proposed that Congress should be given much greater power over the states
o. the part of the government that carries out laws
p. each branch of the government has different and separate powers
q. plan for national government where states would keep their freedom and independence
r. to refuse to sign into law
s. an order that commanded that the Northwest Territory be divided into smaller territories
t. refers to the national government

Notes for Home: Your child learned about the formation of a new government for the United States.
Home Activity: Write each vocabulary word or its definition on a blank index card. Then read each card to your child, having him or her provide the missing word or definition.

Bottom-right worksheet

Name _____ Date _____

Lesson Review

Lesson 1: A Weak Government

Use with Pages 338–343.

Directions: Complete the following fact-and-conclusion chart. In each box at left, write one fact to support the conclusion. You may use your textbook.

Facts

- Congress could not pass laws to collect taxes to run the government.
- There were no branches of government to enforce or interpret laws.
- There was no uniform standard of currency.
- The government could not pass laws regarding foreign trade.
- Protests like Shays' Rebellion were occurring.

Conclusion

The Articles of Confederation created a weak form of government.

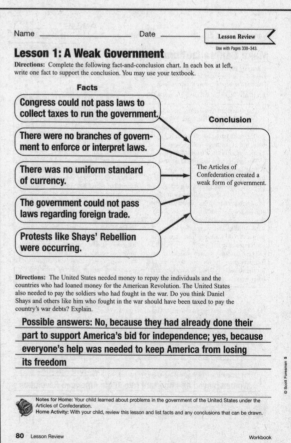

Directions: The United States needed money to repay the individuals and the countries who had loaned money for the American Revolution. The United States also needed to pay the soldiers who had fought in the war. Do you think Daniel Shays and others like him who fought in the war should have been taxed to pay the country's war debts? Explain.

Possible answers: No, because they had already done their part to support America's bid for independence; yes, because everyone's help was needed to keep America from losing its freedom

Notes for Home: Your child learned about problems in the government of the United States under the Articles of Confederation.
Home Activity: With your child, review this lesson and list facts and any conclusions that can be drawn.

Lesson 2: Debate in Philadelphia

Directions: Describe each of the following three terms in your own words. Relate each term to at least one of the other terms. Finally, answer question 4. You may use your textbook.

1. Constitutional Convention

   A group of representatives met in Philadelphia with the goal of revising the Articles of Confederation. After a great deal of discussion, they ended up agreeing on the Great Compromise and other compromises and wrote a new constitution.

2. Virginia Plan

   During the Constitutional Convention, Southerners proposed that the Virginia Plan replace the Articles of Confederation. The plan called for a stronger central government with an executive and a judicial branch. It also stated that states with larger populations should have more congressional representatives than smaller states.

3. Great Compromise

   The Great Compromise was an agreement between the Virginia Plan and the New Jersey Plan. It would create two houses in Congress. Each state would have equal representation in the Senate but have representation based on population in the House of Representatives.

4. Why was a government with three branches considered to be a compromise?

   Possible answer: The three branches of government provide a system of checks and balances that does not allow any one branch to be all-powerful. It is a compromise because it is a strong form of government, yet the people still have control.

Notes for Home: Your child learned about the creation of the United States Constitution.
Home Activity: With your child, talk about an event in your child's life when he or she had to compromise.

Lesson 3: Ratifying the Constitution

Directions: A flowchart is a diagram that shows, step by step, a process of how something works or happens. Complete the flowchart using the items in the box.

Antifederalists	*The Federalist* essays explained the weaknesses of Antifederalist arguments.
A Bill of Rights is promised.	All 13 states ratify the Constitution, making it the supreme law of the land.
Federalists	This group feared that the central government would pass laws that were not suitable for all parts of the country.

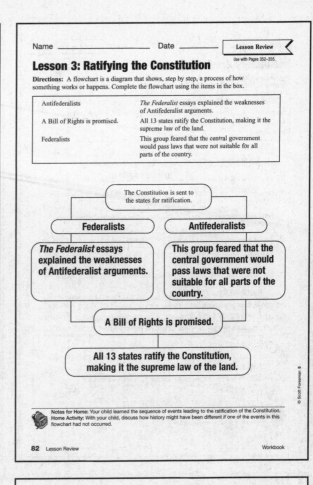

The Constitution is sent to the states for ratification.

Federalists — **Antifederalists**

The Federalist essays explained the weaknesses of Antifederalist arguments. — **This group feared that the central government would pass laws that were not suitable for all parts of the country.**

A Bill of Rights is promised.

All 13 states ratify the Constitution, making it the supreme law of the land.

Notes for Home: Your child learned the sequence of events leading to the ratification of the Constitution.
Home Activity: With your child, discuss how history might have been different if one of the events in this flowchart had not occurred.

Gather and Report Information

Suppose you were going to write a report on the first Vice-President of the United States. Think of the information you would need to write your report.

Directions: Read the information about gathering and reporting information. Answer the questions that follow.

1. An encyclopedia has the following entries. Which one will you need?
   - ● Adams, John (1735–1826) Second President of the United States
   - Ⓑ Adams, John Couch (1819–1892) English astronomer
   - Ⓒ Adams, John Quincy (1767–1848) Sixth President of the United States
   - Ⓓ Adams, Samuel (1722–1803) Signer of the Declaration of Independence

2. Explain the reasoning behind your answer to question 1.

   Possible answer: It is very possible that the person who was the second President might have been the first Vice-President.

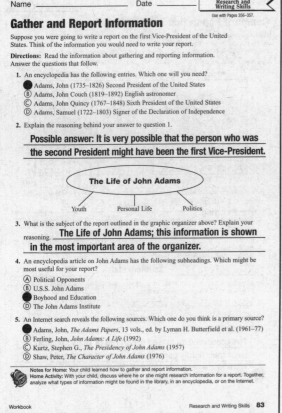

The Life of John Adams

Youth   Personal Life   Politics

3. What is the subject of the report outlined in the graphic organizer above? Explain your reasoning. **The Life of John Adams; this information is shown in the most important area of the organizer.**

4. An encyclopedia article on John Adams has the following subheadings. Which might be most useful for your report?
   - Ⓐ Political Opponents
   - Ⓑ U.S.S. John Adams
   - ● Boyhood and Education
   - Ⓓ The John Adams Institute

5. An Internet search reveals the following sources. Which one do you think is a primary source?
   - ● Adams, John, *The Adams Papers*, 13 vols., ed. by Lyman H. Butterfield et al. (1961–77)
   - Ⓑ Ferling, John, *John Adams: A Life* (1992)
   - Ⓒ Kurtz, Stephen G., *The Presidency of John Adams* (1957)
   - Ⓓ Shaw, Peter, *The Character of John Adams* (1976)

Notes for Home: Your child learned how to gather and report information.
Home Activity: With your child, discuss where he or she might research information for a report. Together, analyze what types of information might be found in the library, in an encyclopedia, or on the Internet.

Vocabulary Review

Directions: Circle the vocabulary term that best completes each sentence. Not all terms will be used.

Articles of Confederation	Constitutional Convention	checks and balances
ratify	Virginia Plan	veto
legislative branch	New Jersey Plan	Federalists
executive branch	compromise	federal
judicial branch	Great Compromise	Antifederalists
inflation	Three-Fifths Compromise	*The Federalist*
Shays' Rebellion	Preamble	amendment
Northwest Ordinance	reserved powers	Bill of Rights
delegate	separation of powers	

1. The (legislative branch, ⓙudicial branch) of government is responsible for the court system.

2. To approve a bill is to (veto, ratify) it.

3. The (compromise, delegate) from my state comes from my town.

4. The system of (checks and balances, separation of powers) guards against any one branch of the government becoming too powerful.

5. (Compromise, Inflation) happens when prices rise very quickly.

6. An addition or change is known as a(n) (amendment, veto).

7. The (Northwest Ordinance, Articles of Confederation) turned out to be a plan of government that was too weak in many people's opinions.

8. In a (compromise, constitution), each side gives up something to reach an agreement.

9. The (Three-Fifths Compromise, Bill of Rights) is a group of ten amendments to the Constitution.

10. The word (federal, inflation) refers to the national government.

11. (Reserved powers, Checks and balances) are powers left strictly to state governments.

12. The (Federalists, Antifederalists) were a group that wanted a strong national government.

Notes for Home: Your child learned how the United States struggled to find a suitable form of government.
Home Activity: With your child, study the vocabulary definitions by playing a question-and-answer game. First, read your child a definition. Then have him or her give the answer in question form, such as "What are the Articles of Confederation?"

Vocabulary Preview

Directions: Choose the vocabulary term from the box that best completes each sentence. Not all terms will be used. Write the word on the line provided. You may use your glossary.

electoral college	pioneer	neutral	War of 1812
inauguration	frontier	Battle of Tippecanoe	national anthem
Cabinet	Louisiana Purchase	War Hawks	Battle of New Orleans
political party			

1. The **Louisiana Purchase** doubled the size of the United States.

2. "The Star-Spangled Banner" is the **national anthem** of the United States.

3. The **electoral college** is made up of people chosen by each state to vote for the President and Vice-President.

4. Daniel Boone was a **pioneer**, or person who pushed westward searching for land to settle.

5. To remain **neutral** is not to take sides.

6. A **political party** is an organized group of people who share a view of what government should be and do.

7. The **Battle of Tippecanoe** was fought in the present-day state of Indiana between United States forces and Tecumseh's soldiers.

8. The **Battle of New Orleans** took place after the official end to the War of 1812 because the news had not yet arrived from Europe.

9. The **War of 1812** is remembered for dramatic battles at sea.

10. **Inauguration** is the ceremony when a newly elected President swears loyalty to the Constitution and takes office.

11. The **frontier** is the edge of settlement for early settlers who pushed westward.

12. Members of Congress who pressed for war against Britain were known as **War Hawks**.

Notes for Home: Your child learned about the first struggles in our new nation.
Home Activity: With your child, practice spelling and defining the vocabulary words by creating a puzzle or writing each term in an original sentence.

Lesson 1: Washington as President

Directions: Match each name in the box to its description. Write the name on the line provided. Names may be used more than once.

George Washington	Thomas Jefferson	Benjamin Banneker
Alexander Hamilton	Pierre L'Enfant	John Adams

1. **Alexander Hamilton** He had plans to set up a national bank.

2. **George Washington** He was elected President by the electoral college in a unanimous vote.

3. **Thomas Jefferson** He was the secretary of state under Washington.

4. **Thomas Jefferson** He was a member of the Democratic-Republican party.

5. **Alexander Hamilton** He was the secretary of the treasury under Washington.

6. **Pierre L'Enfant** He designed the city of Washington, D.C.

7. **Thomas Jefferson** He opposed setting up a national bank.

8. **John Adams** He was the first President to live in the President's House.

9. **George Washington** Originally, he didn't want to become President.

10. **John Adams** He was the second President of the United States.

11. **Alexander Hamilton** He believed in a strong national government.

12. **Benjamin Banneker** He was an astronomer who helped survey the land where Washington, D.C., was built.

13. **Alexander Hamilton** He was a member of the Federalist political party.

14. **Thomas Jefferson** He wanted the country to remain a land of small farmers and skilled crafts workers.

15. **George Washington** He was "First in war, first in peace, and first in the hearts of his countrymen."

Notes for Home: Your child learned about events that took place under President George Washington and Vice-President John Adams.
Home Activity: With your child, talk about how the U.S. government would be different today if two political parties had not developed.

Lesson 2: Jefferson Looks West

Directions: Complete each sentence with information from Lesson 2. You may use your textbook.

1. Thomas Jefferson was the **third** President of the United States.

2. Jefferson believed that the power of government belonged in the hands of the **people**.

3. In search of new lands to settle, Americans began moving **west** long before Jefferson became President.

4. Daniel Boone, an early pioneer, created the trail known as the **Wilderness Road**.

5. Boone led many pioneers through the **Cumberland Gap**, across the Appalachian Mountains.

6. Settlers along the Ohio and Mississippi Rivers used these waterways as **trade** routes to ship their products south.

7. Goods shipped along the Mississippi went to the Spanish-controlled port of **New Orleans** and then to the East Coast and Europe.

8. The United States doubled in size with the **Louisiana Purchase**, acquiring land that stretched from the Mississippi River to the Rocky Mountains.

9. Jefferson was interested in the lands to the west and chose **Lewis and Clark** to head an expedition to explore the unknown area.

10. The expedition to explore the West included the help of a French trapper and his Shoshone wife, **Sacagawea**, who served as a guide and interpreter for the expedition.

Notes for Home: Your child learned about changes in the nation under President Thomas Jefferson.
Home Activity: With your child, examine a map of the United States and list the present-day states that would not be part of the United States if not for the Louisiana Purchase and the Lewis and Clark expedition.

Compare Population Density Maps

Population density maps show how many people live in an area. Comparing population density maps of the same area from different time periods can show how the population changed over time. In the maps below, each dot represents 200 enslaved persons.

Directions: Study the maps. Answer the questions that follow in the spaces provided.

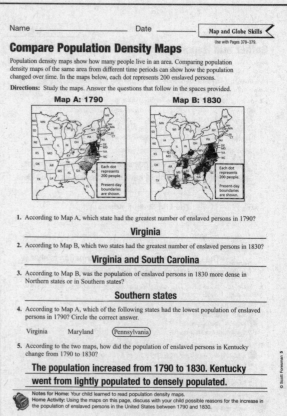

Map A: 1790   Map B: 1830

Each dot represents 200 people. Present-day boundaries are shown.

1. According to Map A, which state had the greatest number of enslaved persons in 1790?
   Virginia

2. According to Map B, which two states had the greatest number of enslaved persons in 1830?
   Virginia and South Carolina

3. According to Map B, was the population of enslaved persons in 1830 more dense in Northern states or in Southern states?
   Southern states

4. According to Map A, which of the following states had the lowest population of enslaved persons in 1790? Circle the correct answer.
   Virginia   Maryland   (Pennsylvania)

5. According to the two maps, how did the population of enslaved persons in Kentucky change from 1790 to 1830?
   The population increased from 1790 to 1830. Kentucky went from lightly populated to densely populated.

Notes for Home: Your child learned to read population density maps.
Home Activity: Using the maps on this page, discuss with your child possible reasons for the increase in the population of enslaved persons in the United States between 1790 and 1830.

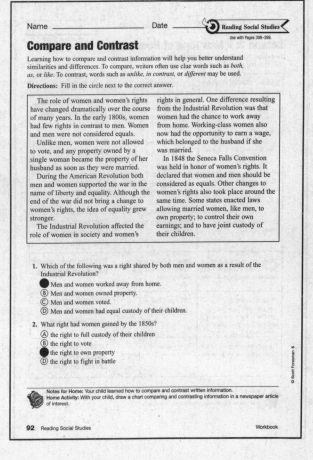

Panel 1 (page 89)

Name _____ Date _____

Lesson 3: Another War with Britain

Directions: Read each pair of cause-and-effect statements. Label each statement *Cause* or *Effect* in the space provided. Draw an arrow from the cause to the effect.

1. Cause
France and Britain are at war. Neither wants the other to receive supplies from the United States. →

Effect
Both France and Britain interfere with U.S. shipping.

2. Effect
U.S. trade with other countries is almost completely cut off. ←

Cause
The British Navy seizes U.S. sailors and cargo.

3. Effect
The Battle of Tippecanoe between U.S. forces and Native Americans is led by Shawnee leader Tecumseh. ←

Cause
Shawnee leader Tecumseh unites Native Americans to resist the settlement of pioneers.

4. Cause
The United States wants to end British-supported attacks against settlers on the frontier and to take Canada from the British. →

Effect
America declares war on Britain. The War of 1812 lasts for two and one-half years.

5. Effect
The American warship *Constitution* receives the nickname "Old Ironsides." ←

Cause
In a battle between the United States and the British off the east coast of Canada, British cannonballs seem to bounce off the sides of the American warship *Constitution*.

Directions: Answer the following question in the space provided.

What is one unfulfilled American expectation of the War of 1812?

The United States never gained control of Canada.

Notes for Home: Your child learned about why the United States went to war with Britain in 1812.
Home Activity: With your child, discuss how things might be different today if the United States still had an adversarial relationship with Britain. Ask whether he or she thinks the United States and Britain will ever declare war with each other in the future. Why or why not?

Panel 2 (page 90)

Name _____ Date _____

Vocabulary Review

Directions: Complete the crossword puzzle using the clues below and the vocabulary words from Chapter 11.

Crossword answers: PIONEER, NEW WORLD, POLITICAL, FEUTRAL, INAUGURATION, FORT, LOUISIANA PURCHASE, HAWKS, ORLEANS, WAR, CABINET, TIPPECANOE, ANTHEM, ELECTORAL

Across
1. An early settler who moved westward
4. A _____ party is an organized group of people who share a view of what government should be and do.
5. This ceremony is held when a newly elected President swears loyalty to the Constitution and takes office.
9. Agreement that doubled the size of the United States with land bought from the French
10. The _____ of 1812 is remembered for dramatic battles at sea.
11. The heads of certain government departments are known as this. These heads advise and help the President.
12. The official song of the United States is its national _____.
13. The _____ college is made up of people chosen by each state to vote for the President and Vice-President.

Down
2. The Battle of _____ took place after a treaty ending the war had been signed in Europe.
3. The edge of settlement for those who pushed westward
6. Not taking sides
7. The Battle of _____ was fought in the present-day state of Indiana between U.S. forces and Tecumseh's soldiers.
8. Members of Congress who pressed for war against Britain were known as War _____.

Notes for Home: Your child learned about developments in the United States during the first presidency and thereafter.
Home Activity: With your child, create a word-search puzzle using the vocabulary terms. Create clues from the words' definitions.

Panel 3 (page 91)

Name _____ Date _____

UNIT 5 Project Two Sides

Use with Page 392.

Directions: In a group, use your textbook and other references to research questions and answers for all roles. Then hold a press conference about the ratification of the Bill of Rights.

1. Questions a news reporter might ask a Federalist:
_____
_____

2. A Federalist's answers:
_____
_____

3. Questions a news reporter might ask an Antifederalist:
_____
_____

4. An Antifederalist's answers:
_____
_____

5. In the press conference, my role is (✔ one):
___ Federalist ___ Antifederalist ___ News reporter

6. My argument (✔ one) for ___ or against ___ ratifying the Bill of Rights is _____

Most Antifederalists supported the Bill of Rights, which protected individual rights against government. Review students' roles to ensure they support arguments for or against ratification.

✔ Checklist for Students
___ I wrote my arguments for or against ratifying the Bill of Rights.
___ I wrote questions and answers on behalf of the news reporter, Federalists, and Antifederalists.
___ I chose a role to play in the press conference.
___ I helped stage the classroom press coverage.

Notes for Home: Your child learned how Federalists and Antifederalists viewed the Bill of Rights.
Home Activity: With your child, discuss the importance of listening to opposing points of view. Give personal examples.

Panel 4 (page 92)

Name _____ Date _____

Compare and Contrast

Learning how to compare and contrast information will help you better understand similarities and differences. To compare, writers often use clue words such as *both*, *as*, or *like*. To contrast, words such as *unlike*, *in contrast*, or *different* may be used.

Directions: Fill in the circle next to the correct answer.

The role of women and women's rights have changed dramatically over the course of many years. In the early 1800s, women had few rights in contrast to men. Women and men were not considered equals.

Unlike men, women were not allowed to vote, and any property owned by a single woman became the property of her husband as soon as they were married.

During the American Revolution both men and women supported the war in the name of liberty and equality. Although the end of the war did not bring a change to women's rights, the idea of equality grew stronger.

The Industrial Revolution affected the role of women in society and women's rights in general. One difference resulting from the Industrial Revolution was that women had the chance to work away from home. Working-class women also now had the opportunity to earn a wage, which belonged to the husband if she was married.

In 1848 the Seneca Falls Convention was held in honor of women's rights. It declared that women and men should be considered as equals. Other changes to women's rights also took place around the same time. Some states enacted laws allowing married women, like men, to own property; to control their own earnings; and to have joint custody of their children.

1. Which of the following was a right shared by both men and women as a result of the Industrial Revolution?
● Men and women worked away from home.
Ⓑ Men and women owned property.
Ⓒ Men and women voted.
Ⓓ Men and women had equal custody of their children.

2. What right had women gained by the 1850s?
Ⓐ the right to full custody of their children
Ⓑ the right to vote
● the right to own property
Ⓓ the right to fight in battle

Notes for Home: Your child learned how to compare and contrast written information.
Home Activity: With your child, draw a chart comparing and contrasting information in a newspaper article of interest.

Vocabulary Preview

Use with Chapter 12.

Directions: Match each vocabulary term to its definition. Write the term in the space provided. Not all words will be used.

nationalism	Industrial Revolution	reform
Era of Good Feelings	manufacture	revival
Monroe Doctrine	technology	temperance
suffrage	cotton gin	abolitionist
Indian Removal Act	mechanical reaper	Seneca Falls Convention
Trail of Tears	canal	

1. **Seneca Falls Convention** — A convention called to take a stand for women's rights

2. **Trail of Tears** — The terrible journey forced upon the Cherokee to move to Indian Territory

3. **Monroe Doctrine** — A statement that warned European nations against considering the American continents for future colonization

4. **cotton gin** — A machine invented to clean the seeds out of cotton

5. **abolitionist** — A reformer who attacked slavery

6. **Industrial Revolution** — A time when people began producing goods by machine rather than by hand

7. **Indian Removal Act** — Act that ordered Native Americans of the southern United States be moved west of the Mississippi River

8. **Era of Good Feelings** — A time when disagreements about national issues grew quiet

9. **suffrage** — The right to vote

10. **nationalism** — The idea that all people should pull together with a sense of strong pride in their country

11. **temperance** — Moderation

12. **reform** — Change

![book] **Notes for Home:** Your child learned vocabulary dealing with the mid-1800s, a time of growth and change in the United States.
Home Activity: Ask your child to use these terms to summarize the turbulent events in the United States during this time.

Lesson 1: The United States Turns Fifty

Use with Pages 402–406.

Directions: Match the events and descriptions in the box below with the President who was in office when they took place. Write each event in the space provided.

Issued warning to European nations not to consider the American continents as subject for future colonization
Headed a new political party, the Democrats
Era of Good Feelings enjoyed
Florida purchased from Spain for $5 million
Native Americans in the southern states forced to move west of the Mississippi
Known as "the man of the people"
Military leader and self-taught lawyer
Encouraged nationalism

President James Monroe	President Andrew Jackson
Encouraged nationalism	Military leader and self-taught lawyer
Era of Good Feelings enjoyed	
Florida purchased from Spain for $5 million	Headed a new political party, the Democrats
Issued warning to European nations not to consider the American continents as subject for future colonization	Known as "the man of the people"
	Native Americans living in the southern states forced to move west of the Mississippi

Critical Thinking: Compare and contrast how the United States expanded its borders under Presidents Monroe and Jackson.

Under Monroe, the United States purchased Florida from Spain. Under Jackson, Native American lands were taken to make way for settlers, and Native Americans were forced to move.

![book] **Notes for Home:** Your child learned about the early expansion of the United States.
Home Activity: Review the lesson with your child, and make a time line of the key events of the United States first 50 years.

Lesson 2: A New Kind of Revolution

Use with Pages 408–413.

Directions: Complete the chart by filling in the last column with one benefit of the following inventions. You may use your textbook.

Before the Invention	Invention	Benefit
There were no factories to spin cotton in the United States.	Samuel Slater built the first cotton-spinning mill in the United States.	The United States could produce its own cloth.
Cleaning seeds out of cotton was slow and difficult work.	Eli Whitney invented the cotton gin.	Production increased by 50 times.
Crops were harvested by hand.	Cyrus McCormick built the mechanical reaper.	It made harvesting wheat easier.
Iron plows were used to clear land.	John Deere developed the steel plow.	Steel plows cut through soil more easily than older plows.
Boats powered by sails or oars had difficulties traveling upstream, against the current.	Robert Fulton invented a riverboat powered by a steam engine.	Travel upstream, against the current, was faster.
Water transportation was cheaper than land transportation, but water routes did not flow in all parts of the country.	The Erie Canal was constructed.	The Erie Canal linked the Great Lakes and the Atlantic Ocean.
Horse-drawn wagons pulled heavy loads on rough roads.	Peter Cooper built a steam-powered locomotive.	Locomotives soon replaced horses carrying heavy loads.

![book] **Notes for Home:** Your child learned about inventions of the Industrial Revolution.
Home Activity: Discuss inventions that help people work more quickly, more cheaply, and with less effort. What new inventions might help us in the near future?

Read a Cross-Section Diagram

Use with Pages 414–415.

A cross-section diagram is a drawing that shows a view of something as if you could slice through it. Cross-section diagrams can show you how something works. This cross-section diagram shows you how the cotton gin worked.

Directions: Study the diagram and answer the questions that follow.

Eli Whitney's Cotton Gin

2. Handle is turned to spin cylinder.
4. Seeds are caught in tray.
5. Brushes clean cotton bolls.
1. Fill container.
6. Clean cotton gathered.
container holds cotton bolls
3. Hooks on cylinder remove seeds.
container for cleaned cotton

1. What do the hooks do?

   They latch onto the seeds on the cotton bolls and remove them.

2. What is the first step in using a cotton gin?

   Fill container with cotton bolls to be cleaned.

3. At what step and how are cotton bolls cleaned?

   Step 5: Brushes clean cotton bolls after the seeds are removed.

![book] **Notes for Home:** Your child learned how to read a cross-section diagram.
Home Activity: With your child, create a cross-section of a household appliance to show how it works. Use reference materials as necessary.

T24 Answer Key

Workbook

Page 97

Name _____ Date _____ **Lesson Review**

Use with Pages 416–420.

Lesson 3: The Struggle for Reforms

Directions: Complete the organizer with terms from the box. Write a brief description on the lines provided.

Abolitionists	Revivals
Attack on Bad Behavior	Seneca Falls Convention
Fight Against Slavery	Temperance
Religion	Women's Rights

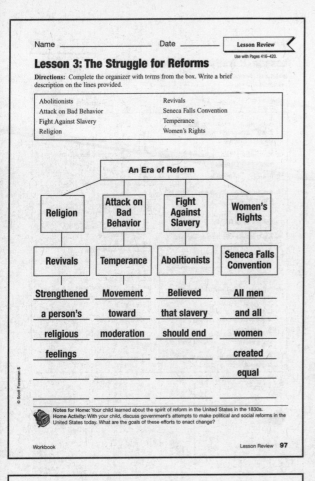

An Era of Reform

Religion	Attack on Bad Behavior	Fight Against Slavery	Women's Rights
Revivals	Temperance	Abolitionists	Seneca Falls Convention
Strengthened a person's religious feelings	Movement toward moderation	Believed that slavery should end	All men and all women created equal

Notes for Home: Your child learned about the spirit of reform in the United States in the 1830s.
Home Activity: With your child, discuss government's attempts to make political and social reforms in the United States today. What are the goals of these efforts to enact change?

© Scott Foresman 5

Workbook | Lesson Review **97**

Page 98

Name _____ Date _____

Use with Pages 424–425.

Writing Prompt: Making Changes

Throughout the nineteenth century, reformers worked to stop child labor. Finally, in 1938 Congress passed the Fair Labor Standards Act. It set 18 as the youngest age for factory workers. Do you think children should be allowed to work? Write about reasons you agree or disagree with the reformers.

Answers will vary.

Notes for Home: Your child learned about different reform movements.
Home Activity: With your child, discuss how life might be different today for women and African Americans if people had not worked to gain equal rights.

© Scott Foresman 5

98 Writing Prompt | Workbook

Page 99

Name _____ Date _____ **Vocabulary Review**

Use with Chapter 12.

Vocabulary Review

Directions: Circle the term that best completes each sentence.

1. Thousands of people were forced to relocate following the terms of the (Seneca Falls Convention, (Indian Removal Act)).

2. A peaceful atmosphere existed in the United States during the ((Era of Good Feelings,) Monroe Doctrine).

3. The ((cotton gin,) revival) increased workers' daily production tremendously.

4. Modern ((technology,) reform) has created many jobs.

5. Goods were sent on the (Trail of Tears, (canal)) to get to market.

6. The ((Monroe Doctrine,) Indian Removal Act) showed foreign powers that the United States was willing to fight for its land.

7. A Wednesday evening ((revival,) reform) was a popular function at many houses of worship.

8. The Second Great Awakening movement supported social (temperance, (reform)).

9. The (Seneca Falls Convention, (Industrial Revolution)) introduced an era of machine-made goods.

10. Many women who supported ((temperance,) technology) tried to stop the drinking of alcohol.

11. The invention of machines helped businesses ((manufacture,) reform) goods on a wide scale.

12. Frederick Douglass, a former slave, was an outspoken (mechanical reaper, (abolitionist)).

13. Many people died along the ((Trail of Tears,) Industrial Revolution).

14. The (revival, (Seneca Falls Convention)) in New York supported women's rights.

15. Women and minorities had to fight for ((suffrage,) temperance).

16. Independence Day celebrations reflect a spirit of (reform, (nationalism)) in the United States.

17. The (Era of Good Feelings, (mechanical reaper)) made it easier for farm workers to harvest wheat.

Notes for Home: Your child learned about changes that Americans wanted to make to improve their lives.
Home Activity: Review with your child how changes in the 1800s affect our life today.

© Scott Foresman 5

Workbook | Vocabulary Review **99**

Page 100

Name _____ Date _____ **Vocabulary Preview**

Use with Chapter 13.

Vocabulary Preview

Directions: Define each term on the lines provided. You may use your glossary.

Texas Revolution __**Texas settlers' fight for their independence from Mexico**__

annex __**To add**__

manifest destiny __**The belief that the United States should expand west to the Pacific Ocean**__

Mexican War __**War declared with Mexico in 1846 over the United States annexation of Texas**__

Bear Flag Revolt __**American settlers in California revolted against Mexico and declared themselves independent.**__

Treaty of Guadalupe Hidalgo __**Officially ended the Mexican War, in February 1848**__

mountain man __**Fur trapper in the West**__

wagon train __**A long line of covered wagons that transported settlers to the West**__

gold rush __**A time when people left their jobs, farms, and homes in search of riches in California**__

forty-niner __**A person who went to California during the gold rush of 1849**__

discrimination __**Unfair treatment**__

Notes for Home: Your child learned terms related to the expansion of United States borders around 1850.
Home Activity: Have your child use these terms to tell how westward expansion helped the United States expand its borders.

© Scott Foresman 5

100 Vocabulary Preview | Workbook

Lesson 1: Settling the South and Texas

Directions: Sequence the events in the order in which they took place by numbering them from 1 to 12. You may use your textbook.

5 Texas settlers decide to fight for their independence from Mexico, and in 1835 the Texas Revolution begins.

1 Spain sells Florida to the United States.

12 The Treaty of Guadalupe Hidalgo is signed, officially ending the war with Mexico.

4 Fearing a rebellion, Mexican leaders pass a law in 1830 forbidding new settlers from the United States.

2 Stephen F. Austin brings settlers to Texas, which is part of Mexico, under a land grant.

10 Mexico still thinks of Texas as part of Mexico and disagrees on the border between the United States and Mexico.

6 Texas leaders form the Republic of Texas on March 2, 1836.

8 Many Americans are against annexing Texas because it would expand slavery in the United States and could lead to war with Mexico.

9 Texas is annexed and becomes a state in 1845.

7 As an independent country, Texas faces problems such as defending itself and having no money. Many Texans want to be annexed to the United States.

3 Tensions grow between Mexico and the settlers from the United States because the settlers bring enslaved people with them to Texas.

11 Efforts to find a peaceful solution fail, and the Mexican War begins on May 13, 1846.

Notes for Home: Your child learned about the settlement of the South and how Texas became part of the United States.
Home Activity: With your child, review the sequence of events in Lesson 1, culminating in Texas becoming a state.

Lesson 2: Trails to the West

Directions: Write the number from each item in Column A on the line next to its example in Column B.

Column A	Column B
1. Period between 1840–1860 when more than 350,000 people moved to Oregon Country	**7** a. wagon train
	11 b. Salt Lake City
2. First settlers to Oregon Country from the United States	**2** c. fur trappers and missionaries
	5 d. Oregon Trail
3. Fur trappers in the West	**9** e. Brigham Young
4. Reason missionaries wanted to move to Oregon Country	**1** f. Oregon fever
	10 g. The Mormon Trail
5. The 2,000-mile route taken to Oregon Country by settlers	**6** h. More settlers headed to Oregon Country
6. Treaty between the United States and Britain settling the border between Canada and Oregon caused this	**3** i. mountain men
7. A long line of covered wagons traveling to Oregon	**8** j. Mormons
8. Followers of the Church of Jesus Christ of Latter-day Saints	**4** k. teach Christian religion to Native Americans
9. Led the Mormons to found their own religious community	
10. Route taken by the Mormons from Illinois across the Great Plains and the Rockies	
11. Place founded by the Mormons in present-day Utah	

Notes for Home: Your child learned about people moving to the West along the Oregon and Mormon Trails.
Home Activity: With your child, discuss the difficulties families encounter as they move from one place to another.

Lesson 3: The Golden State

Directions: Fill in each missing cause or effect. You may use your textbook.

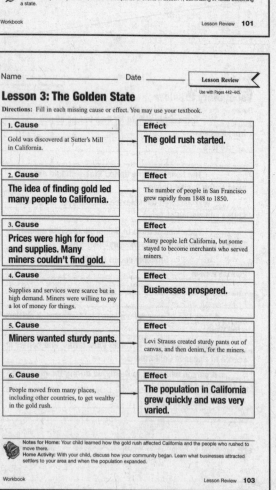

Cause	Effect
1. Gold was discovered at Sutter's Mill in California.	**The gold rush started.**
2. **The idea of finding gold led many people to California.**	The number of people in San Francisco grew rapidly from 1848 to 1850.
3. **Prices were high for food and supplies. Many miners couldn't find gold.**	Many people left California, but some stayed to become merchants who served miners.
4. Supplies and services were scarce but in high demand. Miners were willing to pay a lot of money for things.	**Businesses prospered.**
5. **Miners wanted sturdy pants.**	Levi Strauss created sturdy pants out of canvas, and then denim, for the miners.
6. People moved from many places, including other countries, to get wealthy in the gold rush.	**The population in California grew quickly and was very varied.**

Notes for Home: Your child learned how the gold rush affected California and the people who rushed to move there.
Home Activity: With your child, discuss how your community began. Learn what businesses attracted settlers to your area and when the population expanded.

Evaluate Advertisements

An advertisement tries to sell people goods, services, or ideas. The purpose of all advertisement is to interest people in what the advertiser is trying to sell. Ads for women's apparel were common in the 1800s.

Directions: Read this sample advertisement, and answer the questions that follow.

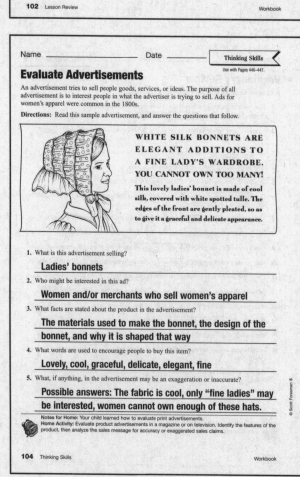

WHITE SILK BONNETS ARE ELEGANT ADDITIONS TO A FINE LADY'S WARDROBE. YOU CANNOT OWN TOO MANY!

This lovely ladies' bonnet is made of cool silk, covered with white spotted tulle. The edges of the front are gently pleated, so as to give it a graceful and delicate appearance.

1. What is this advertisement selling?
   Ladies' bonnets

2. Who might be interested in this ad?
   Women and/or merchants who sell women's apparel

3. What facts are stated about the product in the advertisement?
   The materials used to make the bonnet, the design of the bonnet, and why it is shaped that way

4. What words are used to encourage people to buy this item?
   Lovely, cool, graceful, delicate, elegant, fine

5. What, if anything, in the advertisement may be an exaggeration or inaccurate?
   Possible answers: The fabric is cool, only "fine ladies" may be interested, women cannot own enough of these hats.

Notes for Home: Your child learned how to evaluate print advertisements.
Home Activity: Evaluate product advertisements in a magazine or on television. Identify the features of the product, then analyze the sales message for accuracy or exaggerated sales claims.

T26 Answer Key   Workbook

Worksheet 1 (page 105)

Name _____ Date _____   **Vocabulary Review**
Use with Chapter 13.

Vocabulary Review

Directions: Use the vocabulary words from Chapter 13 to complete each item. Use the numbered letters to answer the clue that follows.

1. Suffering unfair treatment d i s c r i m i n a t i o n
    (1)

2. People from all over the country rushed to California to find riches
   g o l d   r u s h
   (9)   (11)

3. A line of covered wagons traveling west w a g o n   t r a i n
    (2)   (12)

4. Fur trapper in the West m o u n t a i n   m a n
    (3)

5. Texas settlers' fight for independence from Mexico
   T e x a s   R e v o l u t i o n
    (7)   (13)

6. Officially ended the Mexican War T r e a t y   o f
   G u a d a l u p e   H i d a l g o
    (4)

7. Revolt by settlers leaves California independent from Mexico
   B e a r   F l a g   R e v o l t
    (5)   (6)   (8)

8. To add a state to the Union a n n e x
    (6)

9. Someone who went to California during the gold rush
   f o r t y - n i n e r
    (15)

10. Mexico and the United States at war over Texas
    M e x i c a n   W a r
    (10)   (14)

Clue: This policy expanded the nation from coast to coast.

m a n i f e s t   d e s t i n y
1 2 3 4 5 6 7 8 9 10 11 12 13 14 15

Notes for Home: Your child learned how California and Texas became part of the United States.
Home Activity: With your child, locate Texas and California on a map of the United States. Use the scale to calculate how far settlers traveled from the East and Midwest to start a new life in these areas.

Worksheet 2 (page 106)

Name _____ Date _____   [Discovery SCHOOL logo]
Use with Page 454.

UNIT 6 Project Lure of the Land

Directions: In a group, choose a trail that settlers might have taken. Then plan a travel program to share the settlers' experiences.

1. The trail our group chose is _____

2. Some reasons settlers chose this trail:
   _____
   _____
   _____
   _____

3. The (✔) shows some of the details shown on our map:
   ___ trail we chose   ___ mountains and other major landforms
   ___ other possible trails   ___ dangers or points of interest on the trail
   ___ cities or towns   ___ compass rose
   ___ state boundaries   ___ scale
   ___ rivers and other bodies of water ___ key

4. Other materials we will use in our presentation:
   _____ _____ _____

Once groups select a westward trail to research, you may wish to help them locate and identify appropriate source maps from which to create their project maps.

✔ **Checklist for Students**
   ___ We chose a settlers' westward trail.
   ___ We researched reasons travelers used this trail to journey to the West.
   ___ We identified some reasons the settlers chose this trail.
   ___ We planned the features and details for our class.
   ___ We identified props, costumes, sound effects, and other materials.
   ___ We presented our travel program to the class.

Notes for Home: Your child learned about trails settlers used to journey to the West.
Home Activity: With your child, research how early settlers traveled to your community. From what areas did most of your first settlers come?

Worksheet 3 (page 107)

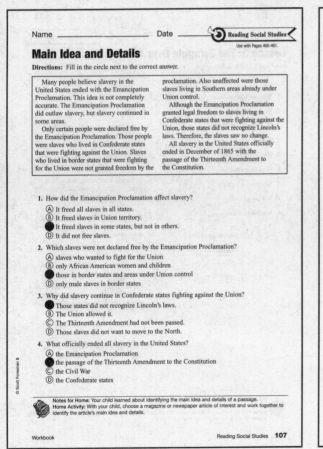

Name _____ Date _____   **Reading Social Studies**
Use with Pages 460-461.

Main Idea and Details

Directions: Fill in the circle next to the correct answer.

Many people believe slavery in the United States ended with the Emancipation Proclamation. This idea is not completely accurate. The Emancipation Proclamation did outlaw slavery, but slavery continued in some areas.

Only certain people were declared free by the Emancipation Proclamation. Those people were slaves who lived in Confederate states that were fighting against the Union. Slaves who lived in border states that were fighting for the Union were not granted freedom by the proclamation. Also unaffected were those slaves living in Southern areas already under Union control.

Although the Emancipation Proclamation granted legal freedom to slaves living in Confederate states that were fighting against the Union, those states did not recognize Lincoln's laws. Therefore, the slaves saw no change.

All slavery in the United States officially ended in December of 1865 with the passage of the Thirteenth Amendment to the Constitution.

1. How did the Emancipation Proclamation affect slavery?
   Ⓐ It freed all slaves in all states.
   Ⓑ It freed slaves in Union territory.
   ● It freed slaves in some states, but not in others.
   Ⓓ It did not free slaves.

2. Which slaves were not declared free by the Emancipation Proclamation?
   Ⓐ slaves who wanted to fight for the Union
   Ⓑ only African American women and children
   ● those in border states and areas under Union control
   Ⓓ only male slaves in border states

3. Why did slavery continue in Confederate states fighting against the Union?
   ● Those states did not recognize Lincoln's laws.
   Ⓑ The Union allowed it.
   Ⓒ The Thirteenth Amendment had not been passed.
   Ⓓ Those slaves did not want to move to the North.

4. What officially ended all slavery in the United States?
   Ⓐ the Emancipation Proclamation
   ● the passage of the Thirteenth Amendment to the Constitution
   Ⓒ the Civil War
   Ⓓ the Confederate states

Notes for Home: Your child learned about identifying the main idea and details of a passage.
Home Activity: With your child, choose a magazine or newspaper article of interest and work together to identify the article's main idea and details.

Worksheet 4 (page 108)

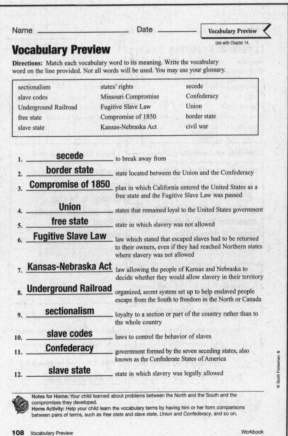

Name _____ Date _____   **Vocabulary Preview**
Use with Chapter 14.

Vocabulary Preview

Directions: Match each vocabulary word to its meaning. Write the vocabulary word on the line provided. Not all words will be used. You may use your glossary.

sectionalism	states' rights	secede
slave codes	Missouri Compromise	Confederacy
Underground Railroad	Fugitive Slave Law	Union
free state	Compromise of 1850	border state
slave state	Kansas-Nebraska Act	civil war

1. **secede** to break away from

2. **border state** state located between the Union and the Confederacy

3. **Compromise of 1850** plan in which California entered the United States as a free state and the Fugitive Slave Law was passed

4. **Union** states that remained loyal to the United States government

5. **free state** state in which slavery was not allowed

6. **Fugitive Slave Law** law which stated that escaped slaves had to be returned to their owners, even if they had reached Northern states where slavery was not allowed

7. **Kansas-Nebraska Act** law allowing the people of Kansas and Nebraska to decide whether they would allow slavery in their territory

8. **Underground Railroad** organized, secret system set up to help enslaved people escape from the South to freedom in the North or Canada

9. **sectionalism** loyalty to a section or part of the country rather than to the whole country

10. **slave codes** laws to control the behavior of slaves

11. **Confederacy** government formed by the seven seceding states, also known as the Confederate States of America

12. **slave state** state in which slavery was legally allowed

Notes for Home: Your child learned about problems between the North and the South and the compromises they developed.
Home Activity: Help your child learn the vocabulary terms by having him or her form comparisons between pairs of terms, such as *free state* and *slave state*, *Union* and *Confederacy*, and so on.

Lesson 1: North and South Grow Apart

Directions: Complete the compare-and-contrast table using information from Lesson 1. You may use your textbook.

Topic	In the North	In the South	Similar or Different?
The way of life in 1850	Most people still lived on farms, but more began working in factories and living in large towns and cities.	People lived a mostly rural way of life. People mostly lived and worked on farms and in small towns.	different
Point of view on tariffs on imported goods	They wanted higher tariffs on imported goods to increase U.S. companies' sales.	They wanted lower tariffs on imported goods to reduce the cost of buying those goods.	different
Point of view on the buying and selling of manufactured goods	They wanted to sell their goods to Americans.	They preferred to buy cheaper goods made in Great Britain.	different
Point of view on slavery	Most states outlawed slavery.	Slavery was profitable, so most states allowed it.	different

Notes for Home: Your child learned about the different views of the North and the South during the mid-1800s.
Home Activity: With your child, discuss instances when your child's opinion or point of view might differ from that of a friend. Brainstorm positive ways to resolve or live with these differences.

Recognize Point of View

Point of view is the way a person looks at or thinks about a topic or situation and describes it. A person's point of view may be affected by his or her experiences and way of life.

Directions: Read the following poem. It was written by a Southern woman during the time when the South had to produce its own goods because it was blockaded by the North. Answer the questions that follow.

> My homespun dress is plain, I know;
> My hat's palmetto, too.
> But then it shows what Southern girls
> For Southern rights will do.
> We send the bravest of our land
> To battle with the foe,
> And we will lend a helping hand
> We love the South, you know.
> Hurrah! Hurrah!
> For the sunny South so dear.
> Three cheers for the homespun dress
> That Southern ladies wear.

1. What is the topic of the poem?

   The ladies of the South will sacrifice to help Southern soldiers.

2. What words does the writer use to show how she feels about Southern soldiers?

   The bravest of our land

3. What words does the writer use to show how she feels about the South?

   We love the South; the sunny South so dear

4. How do you think the writer feels about supporting the South in the war? How do you know?

   Possible answer: The writer is proud to support the South. Her homespun dress, although plain, shows that the South can survive on its own, without luxuries from Europe. This feeling is evident when the writer says "Three cheers for the homespun dress that Southern ladies wear."

Notes for Home: Your child learned to identify the writer's point of view.
Home Activity: With your child, discuss a family situation or a situation at school in which two people had different points of view. Help your child recognize that different points of view can come from different goals or experiences.

Lesson 2: Resisting Slavery

Directions: Categorize each term in the box by writing it in the column of the correct category below. You may use your textbook.

performed acts of cruelty	pretended to be sick
broke the tools they used	separated family members
learned to read	enforced slave codes
required permission to leave plantation	formed the Underground Railroad
used physical punishment	worked slowly

Methods of Controlling Slaves	Ways Slaves Resisted
performed acts of cruelty	broke the tools they used
required permission to leave plantation	learned to read
used physical punishment	pretended to be sick
separated family members	formed the Underground Railroad
enforced slave codes	worked slowly

Directions: Write the missing cause or effect on the line provided. You may use your textbook.

1. **Cause:** Slaves suffered cruel, harsh treatment.
   Effect: **Slaves resisted.**

2. **Cause:** **Slaves led rebellions.**
   Effect: Slave owners tried to prevent slaves from gathering and meeting with one another.

3. **Cause:** Captive Africans aboard the Spanish vessel *Amistad* seized the ship and ended up in the United States.
   Effect: **The Supreme Court decided their fate and released them. All of the survivors returned to Africa that year.**

Notes for Home: Your child learned how slaves reacted to the treatment they received.
Home Activity: With your child, discuss how he or she feels when treated unfairly. Relate this feeling to how the slaves reacted when they were treated harshly and unfairly.

Lesson 3: The Struggle Over Slavery

Directions: Match each item in the first column to its clue or description in the second column. Write the number of the item on the line before its description.

1. Missouri Compromise
2. Fugitive Slave Law
3. Compromise of 1850
4. Kansas-Nebraska Act
5. *Uncle Tom's Cabin*
6. Dred Scott decision
7. John Brown's plan
8. Abraham Lincoln
9. Stephen Douglas

6 The Supreme Court ruled that slaves were not citizens of the United States and had no rights.

5 This book described the cruelties of slavery and won over many people to the abolitionist cause.

4 The people of each territory were allowed to decide whether it should be free or slave.

8 "If slavery is not wrong, then nothing is wrong. . . . [But I] would not do anything to bring about a war between the free and slave states."

2 Escaped slaves had to be returned to their owners, even if they had reached Northern states where slavery was not allowed.

7 A plan to attack pro-slavery people with weapons from the arsenal at Harper's Ferry further divided the North and the South in 1859.

1 The number of slave states and free states was kept balanced when Missouri was allowed into the Union as a slave state and Maine as a free state.

9 "Each state . . . has a right to do as it pleases on . . . slavery."

3 California became a free state, and the Fugitive Slave Law was passed.

Notes for Home: Your child learned about struggles over slavery that threatened to tear the United States apart.
Home Activity: With your child, choose a current controversial issue from the newspaper. Discuss citizens' opposing views and the divisions that can develop.

Lesson 4: The First Shots Are Fired

Directions: Sequence the events in the order in which they occurred by numbering them from 1 to 8. You may use your textbook.

_7_ Lincoln asks Union states for troops to put down the Confederate rebellion.

_1_ Abraham Lincoln is elected President of the United States.

_8_ Some states are angered by Lincoln's call for troops. Virginia, Arkansas, Tennessee, and North Carolina secede and join the Confederacy.

_3_ The Confederate States of America, or the Confederacy, is formed.

_6_ The Confederates attack Fort Sumter, which is surrendered two days later. The Civil War has started.

_5_ Jefferson Davis, president of the Confederacy, asks for the surrender of Union-held Fort Sumter in Charleston, South Carolina.

_2_ The Southern states of South Carolina, Alabama, Florida, Mississippi, Georgia, Louisiana, and Texas secede.

_4_ By Lincoln's inauguration on March 4, 1861, the Confederacy has control of most of the forts and military property in the South.

Directions: Explain each of the following points of view from the time of the American Civil War. You may use your textbook.

1. Explain the goal Lincoln and his supporters hoped to achieve by fighting the Civil War.

   Possible answer: Lincoln and his supporters wanted to preserve the Union.

2. Explain the goal Southerners hoped to achieve by fighting the Civil War.

   Southerners wanted to preserve states' rights and slavery.

3. Why do you think Northerners called Southerners "rebels"?

   Possible answer: Northerners thought the Southerners were rebelling against the established order of government and trying to get their own way.

Notes for Home: Your child learned how different points of view in the United States led to the Civil War.
Home Activity: With your child, discuss how differing viewpoints often can be perceived as threats or hostility. Brainstorm ways that better communication and compromise can be used to prevent these types of misunderstandings.

Vocabulary Review

Directions: Choose the vocabulary word from the box that best completes each sentence. Write the word on the line provided. Not all words will be used.

sectionalism	states' rights	secede
slave codes	Missouri Compromise	Confederacy
Underground Railroad	Fugitive Slave Law	Union
free state	Compromise of 1850	border state
slave state	Kansas-Nebraska Act	civil war

1. The ___**Union**___ was made up of states that remained loyal to the United States government.

2. The ___**Compromise of 1850**___ allowed California to be admitted to the Union as a free state.

3. ___**States' rights**___ is the idea that people of a state can choose the laws that best fit their needs.

4. South Carolina was the first state to ___**secede**___ from the Union.

5. The ___**Missouri Compromise**___ preserved the balance between free and slave states.

6. The states that seceded from the Union formed the ___**Confederacy**___.

7. The ___**Kansas-Nebraska Act**___ allowed people in certain areas to determine whether or not their territory would allow slavery.

8. Although some former slaves had reached the North and found freedom, the ___**Fugitive Slave Law**___ said they had to be returned to their owners.

9. ___**Slave codes**___ did not allow slaves to own land.

10. Slavery was illegal in California and any other ___**free state**___.

11. Harriet Tubman became famous for helping slaves escape to freedom on the ___**Underground Railroad**___.

Notes for Home: Your child learned about differences between the North and the South that divided the nation.
Home Activity: Have your child practice using the vocabulary terms in sentences of his or her own.

Vocabulary Preview

Directions: Circle the vocabulary term that best completes each sentence.

1. The (Anaconda Plan, Reconstruction) was a three-part war strategy to crush the South during the Civil War.

2. Slavery was abolished by the (Thirteenth Amendment, Fourteenth Amendment) to the Constitution.

3. The (First Battle of Bull Run, Battle of Gettysburg) lasted three days and was one of the most important battles of the Civil War.

4. African Americans became U.S. citizens under the (Fourteenth Amendment, Thirteenth Amendment) to the Constitution.

5. At the (Battle of Antietam, Battle of Vicksburg), Union forces blockaded the city and bombarded it for 48 days.

6. (Segregation, Sharecropping) is the separation of blacks and whites.

7. Both the North and the South instituted the (blockade, draft) to get men to fight in the war.

8. The (Gettysburg Address, Emancipation Proclamation) granted freedom to slaves in any Confederate states that were still battling the Union.

9. The time after the war when the country was rebuilding and healing is known as (Reconstruction, segregation).

10. The (black codes, blockade) kept supplies from reaching Southern soldiers.

11. One of the early battles of the war was the (Battle of Gettysburg, First Battle of Bull Run).

12. People in many U.S. cities paid their respects to President Lincoln after his (assassination, impeachment).

13. The (Freedmen's Bureau, Emancipation Proclamation) was established to help former slaves after the war.

14. All male citizens received the right to vote with the ratification of the (Thirteenth Amendment, Fifteenth Amendment) to the Constitution.

15. The (Emancipation Proclamation, Jim Crow laws) enforced separation of blacks and whites.

16. Republicans in Congress called for the (total war, impeachment) of President Andrew Johnson.

Notes for Home: Your child learned about events during and after the Civil War.
Home Activity: With your child, review each vocabulary term and its definition to make sure the term fits in the sentence. Then make your own sentences using the vocabulary terms.

Lesson 1: The Early Stages of the War

Directions: Complete each compare-and-contrast table with information about the Union and the Confederacy. You may use your textbook.

	Supporters of the North	Supporters of the South
Reason for fighting	to preserve the Union	to preserve their way of life

	Northerners	Southerners
Believed advantage over the opposition	Armies needed supplies, and the North produced more than 90 percent of the country's weapons, cloth, shoes, and iron.	The South's more rural way of life would better prepare soldiers for war. The South had a history of producing military leaders.

	Union	Confederacy
War strategies	Three-part plan of action: (1) set up a blockade of the Confederacy's Atlantic and Gulf coasts, (2) capture territory along the Mississippi to weaken the Confederacy by cutting the Southern states in two, (3) attack the Confederacy from both the east and the west.	Defend the Confederacy until the North grows tired and gives up. Northerners, who have nothing to gain, will not fight as fiercely as Southerners. Britain will assist in the war because English clothing mills depend on Southern cotton.

Notes for Home: Your child learned about different attitudes toward war and different strategies used by the North and South during the Civil War.
Home Activity: With your child, discuss possible problems the Union and the Confederacy might have had to consider when forming their war strategies. Ask your child what could have gone wrong in each case.

Lesson 2: Life During the War

Directions: For each main idea, write a supporting detail on the line provided. You may use your textbook.

1. **Main Idea:** News of the war spread in many ways.
   Detail: The news spread through letters, newspaper articles, and photographs.

2. **Main Idea:** As the war continued, both sides had trouble getting more soldiers.
   Detail: Possible answers: The number of volunteers decreased, so both sides passed draft laws; in the Union, men paid $300 to avoid fighting; in the Confederacy, some men paid substitutes to fight in their place.

3. **Main Idea:** Most of the soldiers who died in the Civil War did not die in battle.
   Detail: Possible answer: Disease was the most common cause of death in the Civil War.

4. **Main Idea:** The Civil War did not begin as a war against slavery.
   Detail: Lincoln's goal was to keep the nation united.

5. **Main Idea:** African Americans who wished to serve in the war were not treated the same as white soldiers.
   Detail: Possible answers: At first, African Americans were not allowed to join the Union army; African American soldiers were paid less than white soldiers at first.

6. **Main Idea:** Women contributed to the war effort in many ways.
   Detail: Possible answers: Women ran businesses and farms and became teachers and office workers; some women became spies; some women became nurses; some women gathered supplies for soldiers.

Notes for Home: Your child learned about difficult conditions during the war.
Home Activity: With your child, make a list of the difficulties soldiers and civilians experienced during the Civil War. Discuss how these types of difficulties might have made your family feel about the war, the enemy, and the country.

Workbook   Lesson Review **117**

Lesson 3: How the North Won

Directions: Match each term in the box with its clue. Write the term on the line provided.

Battle of Gettysburg	Ulysses S. Grant	total war
Gettysburg Address	Battle of Vicksburg	Robert E. Lee
Anaconda Plan	William Tecumseh Sherman	Appomattox Court House

1. Place where Generals Lee and Grant met to discuss the terms of the Confederates' surrender of the Civil War **Appomattox Court House**

2. "I would rather die a thousand deaths." **Robert E. Lee**

3. President Lincoln made a short speech at a ceremony to dedicate a national cemetery. In his speech, Lincoln inspired the Union to keep fighting for a united nation and the end of slavery. **Gettysburg Address**

4. A method of warfare designed to destroy the opposing army and the people's will to fight **total war**

5. This three-day battle began on July 1, 1863. It was one of the most important battles of the Civil War. It was an important victory for the North and a costly battle for both sides. **Battle of Gettysburg**

6. Head of the Union forces in the Battle of Vicksburg **Ulysses S. Grant**

7. The surrender of this battle by the Southerners cut the Confederacy in two. **Battle of Vicksburg**

8. The Union blockade at the Battle of Vicksburg was part of this strategy to gain control of the Mississippi River and weaken the Confederacy. **Anaconda Plan**

9. Led soldiers in a destructive "March to the Sea" **William Tecumseh Sherman**

Notes for Home: Your child learned how the North used strategies to win the Civil War.
Home Activity: With your child, brainstorm strategies for winning a game such as checkers, chess, or cards. Discuss the advantages of using a strategy to defeat an opponent.

118 Lesson Review   Workbook

Read a Road Map

A road map shows roads, cities, and places of interest. Drivers use road maps to figure out how to get from one place to another.

Directions: Use the road map to answer the following questions.

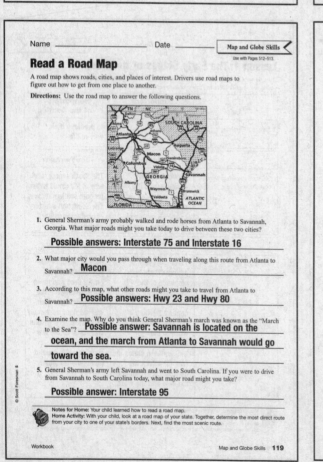

1. General Sherman's army probably walked and rode horses from Atlanta to Savannah, Georgia. What major roads might you take today to drive between these two cities?

   Possible answers: Interstate 75 and Interstate 16

2. What major city would you pass through when traveling along this route from Atlanta to Savannah? **Macon**

3. According to this map, what other roads might you take to travel from Atlanta to Savannah? **Possible answers: Hwy 23 and Hwy 80**

4. Examine the map. Why do you think General Sherman's march was known as the "March to the Sea"? **Possible answer: Savannah is located on the ocean, and the march from Atlanta to Savannah would go toward the sea.**

5. General Sherman's army left Savannah and went to South Carolina. If you were to drive from Savannah to South Carolina today, what major road might you take?

   Possible answer: Interstate 95

Notes for Home: Your child learned how to read a road map.
Home Activity: With your child, look at a road map of your state. Together, determine the most direct route from your city to one of your state's borders. Next, find the most scenic route.

Workbook   Map and Globe Skills **119**

Lesson 4: The End of Slavery

Directions: Define each term or phrase. Use a separate sheet of paper if you need more room. You may use your textbook.

1. Reconstruction **The rebuilding and healing of the country after the Civil War**

2. Thirteenth Amendment **The amendment that abolished slavery in the United States**

3. black codes **Laws that denied African Americans many things, including the right to vote, to take part in jury trials, to own land or guns, or to take certain jobs; allowed unemployed African Americans to be fined or arrested**

4. Freedmen's Bureau **Bureau established to help the 4 million former slaves after the war**

5. Ku Klux Klan **Group formed to restore white control over African Americans after the war**

6. Fourteenth Amendment **Gave African Americans citizenship and equal protection of the law**

7. Jim Crow laws **Laws that enforced segregation**

8. sharecropping **The practice of renting land from landowners and then paying the rent with a portion of the crop produced on that land**

Notes for Home: Your child learned about how the United States changed after the Civil War.
Home Activity: With your child, review the series of changes that took place during Reconstruction and discuss who benefited from each change.

120 Lesson Review   Workbook

Panel 1 (top left)

Name _____ Date _____ **Vocabulary Review**

Use with Chapter 15.

Vocabulary Review

Directions: Use the vocabulary words from Chapter 15 to complete the following sentences. Write the correct word in the space provided. You may use your textbook.

1. **Segregation** _____ is the separation of blacks and whites.

2. The shutting off of an area by troops or ships to keep people and supplies from moving in or out is known as a **blockade**

3. At the Battle of **Vicksburg** _____, Union forces blockaded the city and bombarded it with cannon fire by land and sea for 48 days.

4. **Sharecropping** _____ is the practice of renting land from a landowner and paying rent with a portion of the crop produced on that land.

5. The murdering of a government or political leader is known as an **assassination**

6. Laws that denied blacks the right to vote or take part in jury trials were known as **black codes**

7. A method of warfare that destroys not only the opposing army but also the people's will to fight is known as **total war**

8. In the Battle of **Antietam** _____, Union and Confederate forces clashed near the town of Sharpsburg in Maryland.

9. The First Battle of **Bull Run** _____, one of the early battles of the Civil War, was won by the Confederates.

10. The **Freedmen's Bureau** _____ was established to help the more than 4 million former slaves after the war.

11. **Reconstruction** _____ refers to the rebuilding of the country after the Civil War.

12. The Battle of **Gettysburg** _____ lasted three days and was one of the most important battles of the Civil War.

13. **Jim Crow** _____ laws enforced the separation of blacks and whites.

14. The **Anaconda** _____ Plan was a war strategy designed to "squeeze" the Confederacy.

Notes for Home: Your child learned about how the Civil War divided the nation and what steps were taken to heal and rebuild the country afterward.
Home Activity: With your child, analyze the relationships among the vocabulary terms for this unit. Begin by having your child place each term on a time line for the Civil War era.

© Scott Foresman 5

Workbook   Vocabulary Review **121**

Panel 2 (top right)

Name _____ Date _____

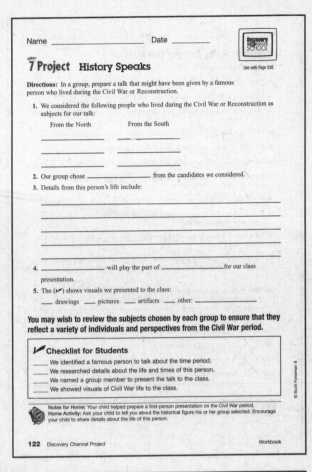

7 Project **History Speaks**

Use with Page 526.

Directions: In a group, prepare a talk that might have been given by a famous person who lived during the Civil War or Reconstruction.

1. We considered the following people who lived during the Civil War or Reconstruction as subjects for our talk:

   From the North   From the South

   _____   _____

   _____   _____

2. Our group chose _____ from the candidates we considered.

3. Details from this person's life include:

   _____

   _____

   _____

   _____

4. _____ will play the part of _____ for our class presentation.

5. The (✔) shows visuals we presented to the class:
   ___ drawings ___ pictures ___ artifacts ___ other: _____

You may wish to review the subjects chosen by each group to ensure that they reflect a variety of individuals and perspectives from the Civil War period.

✔ **Checklist for Students**

___ We identified a famous person to talk about the time period.
___ We researched details about the life and times of this person.
___ We named a group member to present the talk to the class.
___ We showed visuals of Civil War life to the class.

Notes for Home: Your child helped prepare a first-person presentation on the Civil War period.
Home Activity: Ask your child to tell you about the historical figure his or her group selected. Encourage your child to share details about the life of this person.

© Scott Foresman 5

122 Discovery Channel Project   Workbook

Panel 3 (bottom left)

Name _____ Date _____ **Reading Social Studies**

Use with Pages 534–535.

Sequence

Directions: Fill in the circle next to the correct answer.

The United States began expanding westward during the 1800s. This expansion brought change to many people and parts of the nation.

As an increasing number of settlers moved west, the need for cross-country transportation and communication grew. Settlers on the frontier did not want to be isolated from friends and family back East. Several new services were created to meet this need. First was the Pony Express. It lasted about a year until the first cross-country telegraph line was completed. A year later, in 1862, construction of the transcontinental railroad began.

At the same time the nation was laying railroad ties to link the East and West, the Homestead Act was encouraging people to settle the Midwest. The Homestead Act gave land to settlers. In 1877 many African American pioneers took advantage of the Homestead Act and settled Nicodemus, Kansas. Nicodemus became a bustling town and still lives on today as a symbol of freedom and opportunity.

In the Great Plains, Native Americans found their lives changing. In 1868 the U.S. government moved the Lakota people to the Great Lakota Reservation, an area that included the Black Hills. Just six years later, gold was found in the Black Hills, and the U.S. government again tried to move the Lakota. The Lakota refused to leave and defeated the United States in 1876 at the Battle of Little Bighorn, also known as Custer's Last Stand. One year later, the Lakota were defeated and moved to a new reservation.

1. Which of the following happened first?
   ● Lakota moved to the Great Lakota Reservation
   Ⓑ Nicodemus founded
   Ⓒ gold discovered in Black Hills
   Ⓓ Lakota defeated U.S. military

2. Which of the following shows the correct sequence of events?
   Ⓐ Nicodemus founded, Lakota Reservation created
   Ⓑ Battle of Little Bighorn, Pony Express established
   Ⓒ Lakota move to new lands, railroad construction begins
   ● Custer's Last Stand, African American pioneers found Nicodemus

Notes for Home: Your child learned how to sequence events that took place during the expansion of the United States.
Home Activity: Ask your child whether he or she would have liked to have lived during the time when the country was growing and technology was developing. Discuss why or why not.

© Scott Foresman 5

Workbook   Reading Social Studies **123**

Panel 4 (bottom right)

Name _____ Date _____ **Vocabulary Preview**

Use with Chapter 16.

Vocabulary Preview

Directions: Match each word with its meaning. Write the vocabulary word on the line next to its meaning. You may use your glossary.

Pony Express	Homestead Act	exoduster	reservation
telegraph	homesteader	cattle drive	Battle of Little Bighorn
transcontinental railroad	sodbuster	barbed wire	

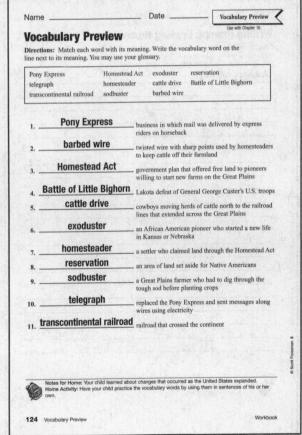

1. **Pony Express** _____ business in which mail was delivered by express riders on horseback

2. **barbed wire** _____ twisted wire with sharp points used by homesteaders to keep cattle off their farmland

3. **Homestead Act** _____ government plan that offered free land to pioneers willing to start new farms on the Great Plains

4. **Battle of Little Bighorn** _____ Lakota defeat of General George Custer's U.S. troops

5. **cattle drive** _____ cowboys moving herds of cattle north to the railroad lines that extended across the Great Plains

6. **exoduster** _____ an African American pioneer who started a new life in Kansas or Nebraska

7. **homesteader** _____ a settler who claimed land through the Homestead Act

8. **reservation** _____ an area of land set aside for Native Americans

9. **sodbuster** _____ a Great Plains farmer who had to dig through the tough sod before planting crops

10. **telegraph** _____ replaced the Pony Express and sent messages along wires using electricity

11. **transcontinental railroad** _____ railroad that crossed the continent

Notes for Home: Your child learned about changes that occurred as the United States expanded.
Home Activity: Have your child practice the vocabulary words by using them in sentences of his or her own.

© Scott Foresman 5

124 Vocabulary Preview   Workbook

Lesson 1: Rails Across the Nation

Directions: Circle the answer that best completes each sentence.

1. In the 1850s thousands of miles of (railroad tracks) paved highways) crisscrossed the East.

2. The journey to the West by wagon or by ship could take (two weeks, (months)).

3. ((Stagecoach,) Pony Express) riders traveled in a horse-drawn wagon that traveled in stages, or short sections.

4. The (wagon train, (Pony Express)) delivered mail faster than was possible by stagecoach.

5. The ((telegraph,) stagecoach) put the Pony Express out of business.

6. Messages were sent along electrical wires in the form of (Navajo Code, (Morse Code)).

7. People were interested in building the ((transcontinental railroad,) stagecoach) to move people and goods across the nation.

8. Central Pacific workers began building tracks heading ((east,) west).

9. Both the Central Pacific and the Union Pacific had difficulties finding enough ((workers,) machines) for the huge project.

10. Union Pacific workers were challenged by ((Native Americans,) buffalo) when the tracks crossed hunting areas.

11. The railroad was completed when the tracks laid by Central Pacific and Union Pacific workers met at ((Promontory Point,) Salt Lake City) in Utah Territory.

Directions: Sequence the events below by drawing a line from each date in the first column to an event from that year in the second column.

1858	a. transcontinental railroad construction begins
1860	b. stagecoach travel begins
1861	c. transcontinental railroad is completed
1862	d. Pony Express delivery begins
1869	e. transcontinental telegraph communication begins

Notes for Home: Your child learned about early travel to the West and the building of the transcontinental railroad.
Home Activity: With your child, sequence the events involved in building the transcontinental railroad.

© Scott Foresman 5

Time Zone Map

A time zone map tells you in what time zone a place is located. With this information you can figure out the time in other places across the country. Regardless of where you live, zones to the east of you are later than the zone in which you are located. Zones to the west of you are earlier.

Directions: Use the time zone map below to answer the questions that follow.

1. Suppose you were in Wichita, Kansas, and wanted to share some good news with your brother in Boston, Massachusetts. He gets home from work at 5:30 P.M. At what time might you place a call from your time zone to reach him at home after work?

   Ⓐ 2:30 P.M.   Ⓑ 2:45 P.M.   Ⓒ 3:45 P.M.   ● 4:45 P.M.

2. Bus, train, and airplane schedules list departure and arrival times according to the city in which each action takes place. Suppose you live in Dallas, Texas, and a relative is visiting from Los Angeles, California. The plane is scheduled to land in Dallas at 3:00 P.M. What time will it be in Los Angeles, when the plane lands in Dallas?

   Ⓐ 12:00 P.M.   ● 1:00 P.M.   Ⓒ 4:00 P.M.   Ⓓ 5:00 P.M.

3. Suppose you live in Las Vegas, Nevada, and you want to watch a live TV broadcast from Washington, D.C., scheduled to begin at 7:00 P.M. D.C. time. At what time should you tune in to the broadcast?

   ● 4:00 P.M.   Ⓑ 6:00 P.M.   Ⓒ 9:00 P.M.   Ⓓ 10:00 P.M.

4. Suppose you used an overnight delivery service to send a package from your home in Seattle, Washington, to a friend in Miami, Florida. The service promises to deliver the package by 10:00 A.M. Florida time. At what time can you call from Seattle to make sure your friend has received the package?

   Ⓐ 1:00 A.M.   ● 7:00 A.M.   Ⓒ 12:00 P.M.   Ⓓ 1:00 P.M.

Notes for Home: Your child learned about time zones.
Home Activity: With your child, practice calculating time in other time zones. You may wish to use TV shows, travel schedules, or phone calls as examples.

© Scott Foresman 5

Writing Prompt: Leaving Home

Long ago, the United States grew as Americans traveled westward. Many people left home for the first time to settle in a new place. Think about your first time away from home. How did you feel? What did you see? Write a paragraph to tell about it.

Answers will vary.

Notes for Home: Your child learned about transportation changes and westward expansion.
Home Activity: With your child, discuss some of the reasons people move. Compare and contrast reasons for moving today and long ago.

© Scott Foresman 5

Lesson 2: Farmers and Cowboys

Directions: Answer the clues below. Then find and circle the answers in the puzzle. Answers may appear horizontally, vertically, or diagonally in the puzzle.

```
T B V J X H O M E S T E A D E R S
G R A S S H O P P E R S L X C T G
O T A W K Y A V N Z C O W T O W N
D Z M N B R J F S I X B U I R D P
L Q E X S O D B U S T E R S Y K T
E U R A Y C M X Z D C V M A H U A
X N I S Z L O N G H O R N S O R F
O E C B G W E N A Q L E Z P M W Y
D R A T C H Y S T Z R W K X E C B
U Y F Z S O D V B I J U D J S O L
S O V I P M L W Y N Z S C T G I
T E K E X Q J E Z O K B T N M A Z
E A R N J B W G Y C V H L T D B A
R S P W Y R X S L A Z J P O W A Z R
F M C A T T L E D R I V E X C L D
H V B Z D P Y K M O W H E A T Q S
```

1. Offered free land to pioneer farmers
2. Settlers who claimed free land offered by the government
3. The ___ railroad helped bring settlers west.
4. Prairie grasses with thick, tangled roots
5. Farmers who had to dig through a layer of sod
6. In the winter, plains settlers faced deadly ___
7. Millions of ___ ate the farmers' crops.
8. Europeans who wanted to move to the Great Plains had ___
9. The Mennonites introduced a hardy type of ___
10. Named themselves after the book of Exodus in the Bible
11. Tough breed of cattle: Texas ___
12. Began in Texas and ended in one of several towns along the railroad
13. Railroad town such as Abilene, Kansas
14. Twisted wire with sharp points

Notes for Home: Your child learned how the Great Plains became an important farming and ranching region.
Home Activity: Discuss with your child that people had to weigh the pros and cons of leaving their homes and moving west. Together, create a chart listing the pros and cons of moving to the Great Plains during the mid-1800s.

© Scott Foresman 5

Lesson 3: War in the West

Directions: Sequence the events in the order in which they occurred. Number the events from 1 (earliest) to 10 (most recent). You may use your textbook.

7 United States soldiers march into the Black Hills hoping to defeat the Lakota and move them onto a new reservation.

3 Government leaders want to move Native Americans onto reservations to make room for expanding railroad lines and new farms, ranches, and mines.

1 Railroads bring many settlers to the Great Plains. Farmers and ranchers begin fencing their land, and herds of buffalo begin to disappear.

4 The United States and the Lakota sign a treaty creating the Great Lakota Reservation, which includes the Black Hills.

6 The United States offers to buy land from the Lakota, but the Lakota refuse to sell.

10 Native American writers and filmmakers continue to tell stories about their people's history and way of life.

8 General Custer and his troops attack the Lakota, and all are killed in a battle known as the Battle of Little Bighorn.

2 Native Americans see that their traditional way of life is being threatened.

9 The Nez Percé surrender to the United States after being chased for 1,600 miles.

5 Gold is found in the Black Hills, and miners illegally rush onto Lakota land.

Directions: Complete the cause-and-effect chart below.

Cause	Effect
Buffalo were hunted for their hides, for sport, and to feed railroad workers.	**Possible answer: The buffalo herds began to disappear, threatening the Native Americans' way of life.**
Possible answer: United States soldiers were sent to capture the Nez Percé and take them to a reservation.	The Nez Percé fled and were pursued for three months by United States soldiers.

Notes for Home: Your child learned about struggles between Native Americans and the United States government as the West was settled.
Home Activity: With your child, discuss the causes and effects of the wars between the Native Americans and the U.S. government. Discuss what major changes were forced on Native Americans.

Vocabulary Review

Directions: Choose the vocabulary word below that best completes each sentence. Write the word on the line provided.

Pony Express	homesteader	barbed wire
telegraph	sodbuster	reservation
transcontinental railroad	exoduster	Battle of Little Bighorn
Homestead Act	cattle drive	

1. Two companies built the **transcontinental railroad** to connect the country by rail.

2. An African American pioneer who started a new life in Kansas or Nebraska was an **exoduster**.

3. **Barbed wire** is used by farmers to create inexpensive fences to keep cattle off their farmland.

4. The government offered the **Homestead Act**, granting free land to pioneers willing to start new farms on the Great Plains.

5. Native Americans were moved to a **reservation**, or land set aside by the government.

6. The **Pony Express** made mail delivery faster than by stagecoach.

7. U.S. General George Custer was killed in the **Battle of Little Bighorn**.

8. A farmer on the Great Plains was known as a **sodbuster** because of the tough soil in that area.

9. Cowboys participated in a **cattle drive** to get their cattle north to the railroad lines.

10. A **homesteader** was someone who took advantage of the government plan to grant land to settlers who would farm the Great Plains.

11. With the invention of the **telegraph**, messages were sent along wires using electricity.

Notes for Home: Your child learned about changes that occurred as the nation expanded.
Home Activity: Practice the vocabulary words by having a spelling bee or a definition bee involving several friends or family members.

Vocabulary Preview

Directions: Write the definition of each term on the lines provided. You may use your glossary.

1. monopoly **A company that has control over an entire industry and stops competition**

2. corporation **A business that is owned by investors**

3. tenement **A building that is divided into small apartments**

4. prejudice **An unfair negative opinion about a group of people**

5. settlement house **A center that provides help for those who have little money**

6. labor union **A group of workers who have joined together to fight for improved working conditions and better wages**

7. strike **Workers' refusal to work until business owners meet their demands**

8. Spanish-American War **The war between Spain and the United States that started when the USS *Maine* exploded in Cuba's Havana harbor**

9. Rough Rider **A volunteer in Theodore Roosevelt's group of soldiers who fought in the Spanish-American War**

10. Buffalo Soldier **Experienced African American soldier who fought against Native Americans on the Great Plains and fought alongside the Rough Riders in the Spanish-American War**

Notes for Home: Your child learned about life in the United States in the late 1800s.
Home Activity: Have your child write each vocabulary term in an original sentence. If he or she has difficulty, find the term in the text and explore how it is used.

Lesson 1: Inventions and Big Business

Directions: Match each person listed in the box below to an invention or accomplishment listed in the chart. Some answers will be used more than once. You may use your textbook.

John D. Rockefeller	Lewis Latimer	Andrew Carnegie
Alexander Graham Bell	Thomas Edison	Henry Bessemer

Invention/Accomplishment	Person Responsible
1. telephone	**Alexander Graham Bell**
2. phonograph	**Thomas Edison**
3. helped make steel a major industry in the United States	**Andrew Carnegie**
4. movie camera	**Thomas Edison**
5. light bulb	**Thomas Edison**
6. long-lasting light bulb	**Lewis Latimer**
7. gave away more than $300 million to help build universities, libraries, museums, and theaters	**Andrew Carnegie**
8. founded Standard Oil	**John D. Rockefeller**
9. new process for making steel	**Henry Bessemer**

Notes for Home: Your child learned about American entrepreneurs and inventors of the late 1800s.
Home Activity: With your child, brainstorm a list of benefits we enjoy today because of the accomplishments of the people listed in the chart.

Lesson 2: New Americans

Directions: Complete each sentence using terms and concepts from Lesson 2. Use an additional sheet of paper if you need more space. You may use your textbook.

1. During the late 1800s, many immigrants came to the United States from **northern and western Europe**

2. During the early 1900s, many immigrants came to the United States from **southern and eastern Europe**

3. Many Europeans left their homes to escape **hardships** such as hunger, poverty, lack of jobs, lack of freedom, and religious persecution.

4. For millions of European immigrants, **Ellis Island** was their first stop in the United States.

5. Many Asian immigrants first came to **Angel Island** and waited there for permission to enter the United States.

6. Upon arriving in the United States, two things most immigrants did first were **find a place to stay** and **and find a job**

7. Most immigrants settled in cities where there were busy **factories** and many jobs.

8. Many immigrants and people from towns and farms moved into cities, causing a **shortage of housing**

9. **Tenements** often provided unhealthy living conditions.

10. Although many immigrants faced **prejudice**, many received help in improving their lives.

11. Some people took jobs in crowded workshops known as **sweatshops**, where conditions often were very dangerous.

12. To fight for better working conditions and better wages, many workers joined **labor unions**

13. Samuel Gompers founded the **American Federation of Labor, or AFL,** to give unions more power.

 Notes for Home: Your child learned about the lives of new immigrants to the United States during the late 1800s.
Home Activity: With your child, discuss the difficulties a new student at school might face and what your child might do to help that person with the adjustment. Compare this to the difficulties immigrants faced.

Lesson 3: Expansion Overseas

Directions: Complete the cause-and-effect chart with information from Lesson 3. You may use your textbook.

Cause	Effect
1. Russia offers to sell Alaska for 2 cents an acre. U.S. Secretary of State William Seward insists Alaska is worth buying.	**The U.S. Senate votes to approve the purchase of Alaska for $7.2 million.**
2. **Gold is found in Alaska.**	Thousands of miners rush north in search of wealth and adventure.
3. American planters discover that the Hawaiian climate is good for growing sugarcane and pineapples.	**American planters establish several large plantations in Hawaii.**
4. Queen Liliuokalani of Hawaii wants native-born Hawaiians to remain in control of the islands.	**American planters revolt against Queen Liliuokalani, and U.S. soldiers support the planters.**
5. Queen Liliuokalani yields her authority to the United States to avoid bloodshed.	**Hawaii becomes part of the United States.**
6. **In 1895 the Cuban people revolt against Spanish rule.**	Spanish soldiers imprison hundreds of thousands of Cubans to keep people from joining the revolution.
7. People in the United States are angered by Spain's treatment of the Cuban people. American-owned businesses in Cuba begin feeling the effects of the war.	**U.S. President McKinley sends the battleship USS *Maine* to Cuba's Havana harbor to protect the lives and property of Americans in Cuba.**
8. **An explosion destroys the battleship USS *Maine*, killing 260 Americans.**	Americans blame Spain for the explosion. Congress declares war on April 25, 1898, and the Spanish-American War begins.
9. **The United States defeats Spain in the Spanish-American War.**	The United States emerges as a world power.

 Notes for Home: Your child learned how the United States expanded and became a world power.
Home Activity: With your child, make a chart comparing and contrasting the ways the United States gained control of Alaska, Hawaii, Puerto Rico, the Philippines, and Guam.

Credibility of a Source

Some sources of information are more believable than others. This is due, in part, to who is presenting the information.

Directions: Read the two passages about General George Armstrong Custer and answer the questions that follow.

Passage A comes from a historical novel. The story is presented as a part-fact, part-fiction presentation of Custer's journal. As you read the words, imagine them to be directly from Custer, himself.

Perhaps I have worshiped my superiors too well with not enough thought of myself. [My wife,] Libbie, says that I have always been too hasty in putting the needs of others ahead of my own.

Passage B comes from a biography. It is based on fact. At times the author includes a personal point of view or conclusion, as well as reports from others who were involved in the actual situation.

What [Custer] did was perfectly in keeping with his nature. He did what he had always done: push ahead, disregard orders, start a fight. . . .

So he marched his men most of the night and flung them into battle when—as a number of Native Americans noted—they were so tired their legs shook when they dismounted.

1. According to Passage A, how did Custer treat his superiors? According to Passage B?

Passage A says Custer worshiped his superiors. Passage B states that he disregarded orders.

2. According to Passage A, how did Custer treat others, in general? According to Passage B?

Passage A says Custer put the needs of others ahead of his own. Passage B states that he marched his men into battle when they were too tired to fight.

3. Which passage has more credibility? Why?

Possible answer: Passage B is more credible because it is based on fact and contains information from actual participants in the events. Passage A is based only partially on fact.

 Notes for Home: Your child learned how to determine the credibility of a source.
Home Activity: With your child, brainstorm various sources of information and discuss the credibility of each.

Vocabulary Review

Directions: Read the following statements. Then write *T* (True) or *F* (False) on the line before each statement. If the answer is false, correct the statement to make it true. You may use your textbook. Not all words will be used.

F 1. A monopoly is any business that is owned by investors.

A corporation is any business that is owned by investors.

T 2. In some cities, poor people received help at a settlement house.

F 3. The workers decided to stage a monopoly until the owners met their demands.

The workers decided to stage a strike until the owners met their demands.

F 4. The African American soldiers who defended Americans and American property in Cuba were known as Rough Riders.

The African American soldiers who defended Americans and American property in Cuba were known as Buffalo Soldiers.

T 5. A volunteer soldier under Theodore Roosevelt who defended Americans in Cuba was known as a Rough Rider.

F 6. When a single company controls an entire industry and stops competition, it is called a corporation.

When a single company controls an entire industry and stops competition, it is called a monopoly.

F 7. A settlement house is a building that is divided into small apartments.

A tenement is a building that is divided into small apartments.

 Notes for Home: Your child learned how industry and immigration affected the United States during the mid-1800s to late 1800s.
Home Activity: With your child, take turns role-playing a situation for each vocabulary term. You may wish to use real-life situations from the text as models.

Discovery SCHOOL

Use with Page 592.

8 Project Invention Conventions

Directions: Make a poster or advertisement for an invention from the late 1800s.

1. The invention we chose is _____

2. The name of the inventor is _____

3. The purpose of the invention is _____

4. Special features of this invention include _____

5. The (✔) shows the benefits of this invention:

___ helping people ___ saving money ___ saving time ___ other: _____

6. Reasons people should use this invention are _____

7. This invention changed the world because _____

8. This is what the invention looked like.

Encourage students to ask questions of each "inventor" as if they are potential customers. Have students respond with details from their research.

✔ Checklist for Students

___ We chose an invention from the late 1800s.
___ We identified the inventor, and we described the invention's purpose, features, and benefits.
___ We made a poster or advertisement for the invention.
___ We included a picture of the invention on the poster.
___ We presented our poster or advertisement to the class.

Notes for Home: Your child researched an invention from the 1800s and advertised its features to the class.
Home Activity: With your child, identify a modern invention you both agree has changed the world. Discuss how it has impacted your life.

Workbook   Discovery Channel Project **137**

Summarize

Directions: Read the passage. Then fill in the circle next to the correct answer.

In the United States, civil rights are guaranteed to all citizens. However, this was not always true. African Americans and other minorities have long struggled for their civil rights in this country.

In 1892, the Supreme Court allowed segregation and "separate but equal" services for blacks and whites. Many African Americans felt that separate services, even in name, were unequal.

Change came about slowly. In 1950, during the Korean War, African American soldiers and white soldiers fought side by side. Four years later, the Supreme Court ruled that the segregation of public schools was illegal. One year later, an African American woman named Rosa Parks inspired the Montgomery bus boycott. In 1956, the Supreme Court ruled that segregation on

public buses also was illegal.

Civil rights leaders such as Martin Luther King, Jr., and Malcolm X, and groups such as the NAACP emerged to support desegregation on all levels. Over time, this period became known as the Civil Rights Movement.

President John F. Kennedy added to the effort by proposing a new civil rights bill to better protect the rights of all citizens. The bill became law in 1964, after Kennedy's assassination.

The Civil Rights Act of 1964 banned segregation in all public places. The Voting Rights Act of 1965 protected all Americans' rights to vote. African Americans could no longer be prevented from voting. This finally gave them the power to change laws that they felt were unfair.

1. What was the direct result of the Montgomery bus boycott?
   - Ⓐ Segregation in the military ceased to exist.
   - ● Segregation on public buses was ruled illegal.
   - Ⓒ Segregation of public schools ended.
   - Ⓓ Segregation in all public places was ruled illegal.

2. How have civil rights changed in the United States since 1890?
   - Ⓐ Separate but equal is considered fair for everybody.
   - Ⓑ A civil rights bill now protects the rights of some citizens.
   - ● Segregation is illegal and all citizens can vote.
   - Ⓓ Segregation in the military is legal.

Notes for Home: Your child learned how to summarize a passage.
Home Activity: Ask your child to summarize a favorite story or event. Remind him or her that a summary has few details. Challenge your child to eliminate as many words as possible from his or her summary without making it ineffective.

138 Reading Social Studies   Workbook

Vocabulary Preview

Directions: Write the definition of each vocabulary term on the line provided. Use a separate sheet of paper if necessary. You may use your glossary.

1. Progressives — **Reformers who worked to improve government**
2. muckraker — **Writer who exposed shameful conditions in U.S.**
3. isthmus — **Narrow strip of land that connects two larger areas**
4. World War I — **War between Allies and Central Powers, 1914–1918**
5. alliance — **Agreement among nations to defend one another**
6. League of Nations — **Organization of nations formed after WWI**
7. Treaty of Versailles — **Treaty signed in 1919 that ended WWI**
8. Nineteenth Amendment — **Gave women the right to vote**
9. Great Migration — **1915–1940s, African Americans moved to North**
10. assembly line — **Method of mass production past a line of workers**
11. Harlem Renaissance — **Cultural movement centered in Harlem, NY**
12. unemployment — **The number of workers without jobs**
13. stock market — **Organized market where stocks are bought and sold**
14. Great Depression — **Severe economic depression begun in 1929**
15. New Deal — **FDR's programs for recovery from Great Depression**
16. Dust Bowl — **1930s drought in Great Plains destroyed farms**
17. dictator — **Leader in complete control of a country**
18. World War II — **War between Allies and Axis Powers, 1939–1945**
19. concentration camp — **WWII prison in which Nazis murdered millions**
20. Holocaust — **The murder of 6 million Jews during World War II**
21. atomic bomb — **Powerful bomb with great destructive force**

Notes for Home: Your child learned about events in the early to mid-1900s.
Home Activity: Ask your child to use each vocabulary term in an original sentence.

Workbook   Vocabulary Preview **139**

Lesson 1: A Time of Reforms

Directions: Complete the chart by filling in the second column with the specific reform or reformer's main purpose or goal. You may use your textbook.

Reform/Reformer	Reform Goal
Theodore Roosevelt	Possible answer: To conserve more land and natural resources
Progressives	To stop unfair business practices and to improve the way government worked
Muckrakers	To uncover shameful conditions in business and other areas of American life
Sherman Antitrust Act	To improve competition by attacking trusts and forcing them to break up into smaller companies
Meat Inspection Act	To allow government inspectors to examine meat to make sure it would not make people sick
Pure Food and Drug Act	To make food and medicine safer by requiring companies to tell the truth about their products
Army doctors Walter Reed and W. C. Gorgas	To drain areas of standing water to decrease the mosquito population and the incidence of yellow fever and malaria

Notes for Home: Your child learned about reforms during Theodore Roosevelt's term of office.
Home Activity: With your child, read the label from any food package and discuss the importance of knowing which ingredients were used in preparing the food. Encourage your child to consider people's food allergies and other health issues.

140 Lesson Review   Workbook

Interpret Political Cartoons

Use with Pages 606–607.

A political cartoon is a drawing that shows people or events in the news in a way that makes you smile or laugh. The goal of political cartoons is to make you think about events.

Directions: Use this cartoon about women's rights to answer the questions below.

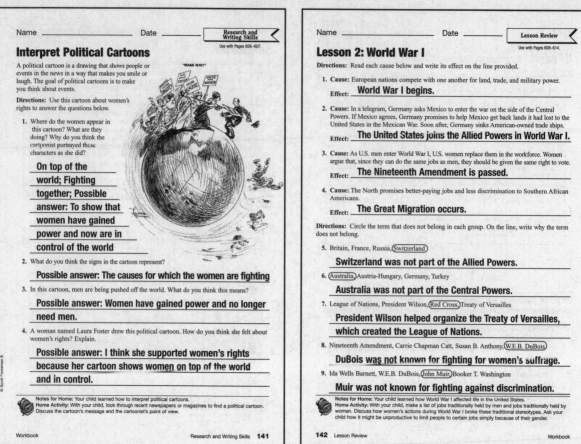

1. Where do the women appear in this cartoon? What are they doing? Why do you think the cartoonist portrayed these characters as she did?

   On top of the world; Fighting together; Possible answer: To show that women have gained power and now are in control of the world

2. What do you think the signs in the cartoon represent?

   Possible answer: The causes for which the women are fighting

3. In this cartoon, men are being pushed off the world. What do you think this means?

   Possible answer: Women have gained power and no longer need men.

4. A woman named Laura Foster drew this political cartoon. How do you think she felt about women's rights? Explain.

   Possible answer: I think she supported women's rights because her cartoon shows women on top of the world and in control.

Notes for Home: Your child learned how to interpret political cartoons.
Home Activity: With your child, look through recent newspapers or magazines to find a political cartoon. Discuss the cartoon's message and the cartoonist's point of view.

Lesson 2: World War I

Use with Pages 608–614.

Directions: Read each cause below and write its effect on the line provided.

1. **Cause:** European nations compete with one another for land, trade, and military power.

   Effect: **World War I begins.**

2. **Cause:** In a telegram, Germany asks Mexico to enter the war on the side of the Central Powers. If Mexico agrees, Germany promises to help Mexico get back lands it had lost to the United States in the Mexican War. Soon after, Germany sinks American-owned trade ships.

   Effect: **The United States joins the Allied Powers in World War I.**

3. **Cause:** As U.S. men enter World War I, U.S. women replace them in the workforce. Women argue that, since they can do the same jobs as men, they should be given the same right to vote.

   Effect: **The Nineteenth Amendment is passed.**

4. **Cause:** The North promises better-paying jobs and less discrimination to Southern African Americans.

   Effect: **The Great Migration occurs.**

Directions: Circle the term that does not belong in each group. On the line, write why the term does not belong.

5. Britain, France, Russia, (Switzerland)

   Switzerland was not part of the Allied Powers.

6. (Australia,) Austria-Hungary, Germany, Turkey

   Australia was not part of the Central Powers.

7. League of Nations, President Wilson, (Red Cross,) Treaty of Versailles

   President Wilson helped organize the Treaty of Versailles, which created the League of Nations.

8. Nineteenth Amendment, Carrie Chapman Catt, Susan B. Anthony, (W.E.B. DuBois)

   DuBois was not known for fighting for women's suffrage.

9. Ida Wells Barnett, W.E.B. DuBois, (John Muir,) Booker T. Washington

   Muir was not known for fighting against discrimination.

Notes for Home: Your child learned how World War I affected life in the United States.
Home Activity: With your child, make a list of jobs traditionally held by men and jobs traditionally held by women. Discuss how women's actions during World War I broke these traditional stereotypes. Ask your child how it might be unproductive to limit people to certain jobs simply because of their gender.

Use with Page 615.

Writing Prompt: New Inventions

The invention of the airplane had a major impact on the way in which World War I was fought. New inventions continue to be developed that change the way we live every day. What could you invent to change your life? Draw a picture of your invention. Write a paragraph to tell about it.

Drawings will vary.

Answers will vary.

Notes for Home: Your child learned about the early planes used during World War I.
Home Activity: With your child, compare and contrast the technology used in World War I to the technology available to the military today. How might technological advances affect the ways in which a war is fought today?

Lesson 3: Times of Plenty, Times of Hardship

Use with Pages 616–622.

Directions: The chart contains important events in the postwar history of the United States. Complete the chart by matching each name or term from the box to one of the statements below. Not all words will be used.

Henry Ford	stock market crash	Charles Lindbergh	radio
Harlem Renaissance	severe drought	Eleanor Roosevelt	Amelia Earhart
Zora Neale Hurston	Social Security Act	Model T	Dust Bowl
bread lines	the Wright Brothers	Langston Hughes	high unemployment
Franklin D. Roosevelt	movies	CCC	cardboard shacks

Advances in Travel	The Roaring Twenties	The Great Depression	The New Deal
The Wright Brothers made the first successful powered airplane flight.	**Movies** moved from "silents" to "talkies," becoming a popular form of entertainment.	Farmers and factories produced more goods than consumers could buy, causing **high unemployment**	**Franklin D. Roosevelt** worked to help the jobless and the poor and rebuild the economy.
Amelia Earhart was the first woman to fly solo across the Atlantic Ocean.	**Radio** brought music, comedy, drama, sports, and news into people's homes.	As a result of the **stock market crash** the economy went from boom to bust.	More than 2 million unemployed young men went to work for the **CCC**
Henry Ford developed the assembly line and produced the **Model T**	A period of cultural growth that produced many famous African American artists was the **Harlem Renaissance**	A **severe drought** hit the Great Plains, earning the area the nickname the **Dust Bowl**	Passed in 1935, the **Social Security Act** provided payments to the unemployed and the elderly.

Notes for Home: Your child learned about good times and difficult times in postwar America.
Home Activity: With your child, make a chart comparing life during the Roaring Twenties and the Great Depression. Discuss how today's economic situation is similar to and different from these two eras.

Lesson 4: World War II

Directions: Complete each summary chart below with information from Lesson 4. You may use your textbook.

Summary

> Possible answer: Hard economic times in Europe cause many people to wish they had a leader who could make their troubles disappear. Some people are willing to sacrifice their own freedom to obtain such a leader.

- In Italy, Benito Mussolini becomes dictator in 1922.
- In Germany, Adolf Hitler becomes dictator in 1933.
- In Japan, a group of military leaders come to power.

Events

Summary

> Important alliances are formed throughout Europe as dictators and military leaders begin trying to conquer and control more nations. The result is World War II.

- Italy, Germany, and Japan begin invading other nations.
- Britain and France join forces against Germany and Italy.
- Germany invades Poland, a nation Britain and France have agreed to protect.

Events

Notes for Home: Your child learned about World War II, its cause, and some of its effects.
Home Activity: With your child, discuss some of the reasons why countries declare war. Discuss whether war is ever justified and, if so, when. Examine with your child some of the far-reaching effects of war.

Vocabulary Review

Directions: Classify the vocabulary terms from Chapter 18 by listing each term in one of the categories below. On the lines below each box, write a sentence summarizing how the terms in that category are related.

The United States

Progressives	unemployment	Harlem Renaissance
Great Migration	stock market	muckraker
Nineteenth Amendment	Great Depression	assembly line
Dust Bowl	New Deal	

Possible answer: During the first half of the twentieth century, the United States went through many changes. Some changes were positive, but others brought difficult times.

Countries Other than the United States

dictator	concentration camp	Holocaust

Possible answer: Some dictators who rose to power in Europe harmed millions of people.

Both the United States and Other Countries

alliance	isthmus
League of Nations	World War II
Treaty of Versailles	atomic bomb
World War I	

Possible answer: The United States and other countries made alliances, developed defense strategies, and fought in wars.

Notes for Home: Your child learned about important events in the first half of the 1900s.
Home Activity: With your child, develop a one-minute oral summary of the first half of the twentieth century. Encourage your child to use as many of the vocabulary terms as possible in the summary.

Vocabulary Preview

Directions: Circle the term that best matches the definition or description.

1. Cold War — (arms control)
   A deal between the United States and the Soviet Union to limit the production of weapons

2. (United Nations) — civil rights
   An organization formed in 1945 consisting of 50 nations dedicated to finding peaceful solutions to international problems

3. (Cold War) — communism
   The long, bitter struggle between the United States and the Soviet Union

4. (Internet) — Iron Curtain
   A worldwide network of computers developed in the 1960s as a communication system that would continue working even after a nuclear attack

5. Vietnam War — (Persian Gulf War)
   War that began in 1990 when Iraq invaded its neighbor Kuwait, hoping to get Kuwait's rich oil supply

6. (civil rights) — legal rights
   The rights guaranteed to all citizens by the U.S. Constitution

7. (communism) — Iron Curtain
   A political and economic system in which the government owns all the businesses and land, and individuals have little personal freedom

8. space race — (arms race)
   The race between the United States and the Soviet Union to build more powerful weapons

9. (Korean War) — Persian Gulf War
   War that began in 1950 when communist North Korean forces invaded South Korea

10. (Iron Curtain) — Cuban Missile Crisis
    The line dividing the continent of Europe into communist and noncommunist countries

11. Cold War — (Vietnam War)
    War that began when communist North Vietnam attacked South Vietnam in an effort to unify all of Vietnam under communist rule

12. (Watergate Scandal) — Internet
    Scandal that forced President Richard Nixon to resign from office in 1974

Notes for Home: Your child learned about U.S. conflicts and compromises in the years after World War II.
Home Activity: With your child, write each vocabulary term on an index card and each definition on a separate card. Shuffle the cards and turn them all face down. Then have your child turn cards over one at a time to match each term with its definition. Be sure to turn the unmatched cards face down again.

Lesson 1: A Dangerous World

Directions: Complete each sentence with information from Lesson 1. Write the answer on the line provided. You may use your textbook.

1. The **United Nations** is an organization formed in 1945 that promised that its 50 member nations would work to find peaceful solutions to international problems.

2. **The United States** and **the Soviet Union** were the world's two superpowers after World War II.

3. In 1945 the Soviet Union had a **communist** government.

4. The United States and the Soviet Union had different views on communism, which resulted in the **Cold War**.

5. At the end of World War II, the nations in **Eastern Europe** were under Soviet control and established communist governments loyal to the Soviet Union.

6. The **Iron Curtain** divided the continent of Europe into communist and noncommunist countries.

7. The **Marshall Plan** was a program launched by U.S. President Harry S. Truman to help the nations of Western Europe recover from World War II.

8. The post-World War II military alliance formed by the United States and the nations of Western Europe was called the **North Atlantic Treaty Organization**.

9. Through the Korean War, the United States was able to keep communism from spreading into **South Korea**.

10. In 1959, under leader Fidel Castro, Cuba became the first communist nation in the **Western** Hemisphere.

11. In 1962 the United States took action to keep the Soviets from setting up nuclear missiles in Cuba. This was called the **Cuban Missile Crisis**.

12. The **hydrogen bomb**, developed by the United States and the Soviet Union, is 1,000 times more powerful than the atomic bomb used in Hiroshima.

Notes for Home: Your child learned about the United States' determination to keep communism from spreading.
Home Activity: With your child, discuss why it might be important to keep communism from spreading in other parts of the world. Ask your child what causes he or she thinks might justify getting involved in a war.

Lesson 2: Struggle for Equal Rights

Directions: Match each term in the box to its description. Write the answer on the line provided.

Harry S. Truman	Rosa Parks	Sandra Day O'Connor
separate but equal	Martin Luther King, Jr.	NOW
Thurgood Marshall	Civil Rights Act of 1964	Shirley Chisholm
civil rights	Malcolm X	Dolores Huerta

1. **civil rights** — The rights that are guaranteed to all citizens by the Constitution

2. **Thurgood Marshall** — Tried to convince the Supreme Court to declare that segregation is illegal under the Constitution

3. **Rosa Parks** — Was the inspiration for the Montgomery bus boycott

4. **Malcolm X** — Civil rights leader who urged African Americans to rely on themselves to bring change

5. **Harry S. Truman** — Ordered an end to segregation in the military in 1948

6. **separate but equal** — Supreme Court language that allowed segregated public services and schools for African Americans

7. **NOW** — Women's rights organization formed in 1966 to fight for fair pay and equal opportunities for women

8. **Shirley Chisholm** — First African American woman elected to Congress

9. **Dolores Huerta** — Helped create a union to improve the lives of migrant farm workers

10. **Civil Rights Act of 1964** — Law banning segregation in all public places in the United States

11. **Sandra Day O'Connor** — In 1981 became the first woman named to the Supreme Court

12. **Martin Luther King, Jr.** — Organized a march in Washington, D.C., in August 1963, calling for an end to prejudice

Notes for Home: Your child learned about women's and African Americans' struggles for equal rights.
Home Activity: Discuss with your child how he or she likes to be treated when playing with other children. Ask him or her to explain the idea of fairness and then work together to brainstorm examples of fair and unfair treatment.

Lesson 3: The Cold War Continues

Directions: Write the letter of the effect on the line beside each cause. You may use your textbook.

Cause

b 1. Soviets launch Sputnik.

g 2. Soviets send the first man to orbit Earth.

k 3. Vietnam gains independence from France.

d 4. North Vietnam tries to unite all of Vietnam under communist rule.

h 5. U.S. armed forces go to Vietnam.

a 6. In April 1975, South Vietnam surrenders to North Vietnam.

i 7. U.S. President Nixon tries to change the Cold War relationship between the United States and China.

c 8. Nixon and Soviet leaders sign an arms control agreement.

f 9. Nixon is involved in the Watergate scandal.

j 10. U.S. President Jimmy Carter tries to bring peace to Israel and Egypt.

e 11. Cold War tensions increase when Soviet troops invade Afghanistan in December 1979.

Effect

a. Vietnam is united under communist rule.

b. U.S. leaders fear that the Soviets will use their new knowledge about space exploration to attack the United States.

c. Each side agrees to limit nuclear weapons, and tensions are eased.

d. South Vietnam resists communism and the Vietnam War begins.

e. President Jimmy Carter objects to the Soviets' attempt to expand their power and refuses to send U.S. athletes to the 1980 Olympics in Moscow.

f. Nixon becomes the only President to resign from office.

g. In an effort to win the space race, the U.S. works toward being the first country to send a person to the moon.

h. Americans are divided on the issue of U.S. involvement in the Vietnam War.

i. Nixon is successful in trying to improve relations and, in 1972, becomes the first U.S. President to visit China.

j. Leaders of Israel and Egypt visit the United States and sign a peace treaty in March 1979.

k. Vietnam is split into North Vietnam and South Vietnam.

Notes for Home: Your child learned about Cold War tensions between the United States and the Soviet Union.
Home Activity: With your child, discuss the positive and negative effects of the Cold War on the United States and the world. Ask your child how the space race and the arms race might have had different results if the United States and the Soviet Union had worked together rather than against each other.

Understand Map Projections

A map projection is a way to show the round Earth on a flat surface. Because Earth is a sphere, all map projections have errors in size, shape, distance, or direction.

Directions: Use the maps on this page to answer the questions below. Use a separate sheet of paper if you need more space.

Map A   **Map B**

Projection: **Mercator**   Projection: **equal-area**

1. Of the two maps shown here, which is the Mercator projection? Which is an equal-area projection? Label the maps accordingly. **Map A: Mercator projection map; Map B: equal-area projection map**

2. What types of distortion are found on a Mercator projection? **The shapes and sizes of the land are more accurate near the equator and more distorted farther away from the equator.**

3. Compare the continent of South America on the two map projections above. What difference, if any, do you see? **On the equal-area projection, South America appears larger and closer to its actual size.**

4. Which map projection should you use to accurately compare the sizes of Greenland and South America? Why? **The equal-area projection; because the size and shape of Greenland would be less distorted**

Notes for Home: Your child learned about map projections and their distortions.
Home Activity: Using the maps on this page or in the textbook, work with your child to compare the distances between lines of latitude on each map. Explain that uneven distances are a clue to one type of map distortion.

Lesson 4: Looking Toward the Future

Directions: Sequence the events in the order in which they occurred. Number them from 1 (earliest) to 10 (most recent). You may use your textbook.

4 The Berlin Wall is destroyed, and several communist governments in Eastern Europe are replaced with elected governments.

1 Newly elected U.S. President Ronald Reagan believes the United States should strengthen its military to block Soviet efforts to expand communism around the world.

7 The United States leads a group of more than 20 nations in Operation Desert Storm, an attack on Iraqi forces in Kuwait.

10 The 2000 U.S. presidential election is one of the closest races in history. George W. Bush wins the electoral college vote, and Al Gore wins the popular vote. George W. Bush is declared President.

3 The Soviet Union and the United States sign an arms control agreement in which both countries agree to destroy some of their nuclear weapons.

5 The Soviet Union breaks up into 15 independent republics, and Gorbachev announces that the Cold War is over.

9 During his second term in office, President Clinton faces a scandal and is impeached.

6 The Middle Eastern nation of Iraq invades Kuwait in an effort to take control of Kuwait's rich oil supply. This begins the Persian Gulf War. The United States must decide whether to help end the conflict.

2 Soviet leader Mikhail Gorbachev begins reforming the country by allowing people more political and economic freedom.

8 U.S. President William Clinton appoints Madeleine Albright as secretary of state. She is the first woman to hold this position.

Directions: In recent decades, many changes have occurred in politics, science, technology, and culture. What is one change that you think will occur in the next 50 years? Why?

Possible answers: Advances in the Internet, virtual reality, other forms of technology, or in other arenas.

Notes for Home: Your child learned about changes in politics and technology that will affect the future.
Home Activity: With your child, discuss inventions and other changes that might take place during this century. Ask whether your child thinks each potential change will have positive or negative effects on the world and why.

Vocabulary Review

Directions: Use the vocabulary words from Chapter 19 to complete the crossword puzzle.

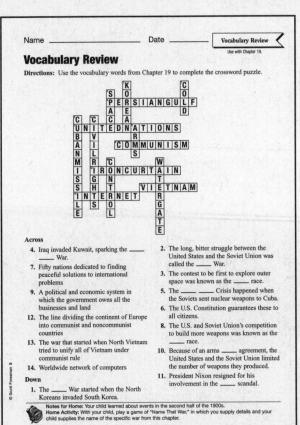

Across

4. Iraq invaded Kuwait, sparking the _____ _____ War.

7. Fifty nations dedicated to finding peaceful solutions to international problems

9. A political and economic system in which the government owns all the businesses and land

12. The line dividing the continent of Europe into communist and noncommunist countries

13. The war that started when North Vietnam tried to unify all of Vietnam under communist rule

14. Worldwide network of computers

Down

1. The _____ War started when the North Koreans invaded South Korea.

2. The long, bitter struggle between the United States and the Soviet Union was called the _____ War.

3. The contest to be first to explore outer space was known as the _____ race.

5. The _____ _____ Crisis happened when the Soviets sent nuclear weapons to Cuba.

6. The U.S. Constitution guarantees these to all citizens.

8. The U.S. and Soviet Union's competition to build more weapons was known as the _____ race.

10. Because of an arms _____ agreement, the United States and the Soviet Union limited the number of weapons they produced.

11. President Nixon resigned for his involvement in the _____ scandal.

Notes for Home: Your child learned about events in the second half of the 1900s.
Home Activity: With your child, play a game of "Name That War," in which you supply details and your child supplies the name of the specific war from this chapter.

---

9 Project Then and Now
UNIT

Directions: In a group, plan a documentary about historic events and advances in technology during a decade from the 1900s.

1. We chose the decade 19___–19___.

2. The (✔) shows which topics we researched:
   ___ historic events ___ technological advances ___ transportation ___ entertainment
   ___ clothing ___ home life ___ education ___ occupations
   ___ other: _____

3. The following people from the decade will speak for the documentary:
   Name: _____ Role: _____
   Name: _____ Role: _____
   Name: _____ Role: _____

4. My role in the documentary is _____

5. Questions about living in the 19___s:
   _____
   _____
   _____

6. Answers to questions about the 19___s:
   _____
   _____
   _____

Have group members confirm that answers to the questions they write are supported by the research they conducted.

✔ **Checklist for Students**
   _____ The group chose a decade from the 1900s.
   _____ The group researched topics about living in the 19__s.
   _____ Roles were assigned for the documentary.
   _____ The group wrote questions and answers about the decade.
   _____ The group presented its documentary to the class.

Notes for Home: Your child participated in a group presentation on a decade from the 1900s.
Home Activity: Discuss with your child your favorite decade of the twentieth century. Describe the clothing, home life, transportation, and important events of this time period.